Young People's
SCIENCE
Encyclopedia

Edited by the Staff of

NATIONAL COLLEGE OF EDUCATION

Evanston, Illinois

Volume 17/Sp-Su

 CHILDRENS PRESS, CHICAGO

Photograph on pages 2 and 99: Saturn V rocket (NASA)
Photograph on pages 3 and 98: Aluminaut (Reynolds Metals Company)

Revised Edition Copyright © 1970
by Regensteiner Publishing Enterprises, Inc.
Copyright © 1963 by Childrens Press, Inc.
All rights reserved. Printed in the U.S.A.
Published simultaneously in Canada.

Library of Congress Catalog Card Number: 67-17925

4 5 6 7 8 9 10 11 12 13 14 15 16 17 18 19 20 21 22 23 24 25 R 75 74 73 72 71

Man has finally begun to conquer space. Here, the earth is seen from the moon as it rises over the lunar horizon

Space Space may be defined as the environment in which all satellites, planets, stars, and nebulae are located. Space is often imagined as an empty area with no end points. This idea is incorrect.

Certainly the universe appears to be limitless. Matter is mostly concentrated in the region of stars, reducing most of space to a near vacuum. But this does not mean that the environmental conditions in space are the same everywhere and at all times. To understand this, a look at man's planet, EARTH, is necessary. It has a gaseous shell which exerts an average of one atmosphere pressure (about 15 pounds per square inch) on the surface. Even a very small change from this pressure is enough to create violent storms.

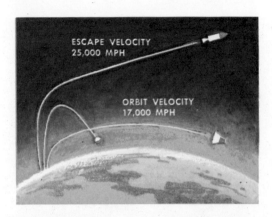

Velocities necessary to overcome gravitation

Earth receives rays from a SUN. This planet's average surface temperature is close to 70° F. Yet, reducing the average temperature by just 10 to 15 degrees would cause another ice age.

The violent events which inspire and awe people, such as hurricanes, earthquakes or spring tides, are purely local events. They may be more spectacular, but are far less influential than those "silent" events on which man's very existence depends. They are so influential because they are far-reaching or even worldwide. Yet how small is "worldwide" on Earth (or any other celestial body) compared to space? Storms are observed on the surface of the sun of such magnitude that a body with the size and mass of Earth would be whirled about like a leaf in a hurricane. Even the unimaginable fury of this event dies away a relatively short distance out in outer space. But weak magnetic and electric fields that gently spread throughout a whole galaxy of stars, hardly noticeable at any local point, can generate the deadly cosmic radiation that has enormous energy remaining unchanged by interstellar or perhaps even by intergalactic distances. Thus it does not necessarily take spectacu-

lar conditions to produce important differences and variations in this environment and climate of space.

What specifically affects the environmental or "climatic" conditions in space? The space environment is controlled essentially by five factors: gravitation, electromagnetic radiation, corpuscular radiation, magnetic fields, and matter.

These factors do not necessarily act independently of each other. Many phenomena in space are the result of combinations and mutual interactions of these factors.

GRAVITATION

Gravitation is the force of attraction caused by large accumulations of matter, as represented by celestial bodies. The strength (pull) of the gravitational field of a body is directly proportional to its mass (not to its size). This means that a celestial body of twice the mass of another body possesses twice the gravitational field strength at a given distance. Thus, the gravitational field of the sun is 332,500 times as strong as that of Earth, because the sun's mass is 332,500 times as large as that of Earth (but its volume is about 1.3 million times that of Earth which means that the sun is only about one-fourth as dense as Earth; the sun is much "fluffier"). But it is not only the field strength alone which is important. The distance from the body is also very significant. For example, near the earth, Earth's gravitational field is about 1,500 times as strong as the sun's field at the distance of Earth's orbit. Thus, for an Earth satellite, the solar gravitational field is unimportant compared to Earth's field. But for an interplanetary space vehicle the sun's gravitational field, though weak, is of great importance. Particularly complex conditions arise where fields of comparable strength but opposing "pull" exist. This is the case in the more distant region of the space between Earth and the moon. Our moon is larger in mass, compared to Earth, than any other moon is compared to its planet. Therefore, throughout some 70 to 95 percent of the distance to the moon, the Earth's field of gravity and the lunar field are of comparable strength, but their pull is in different directions. The resulting complex conditions are the main characteristics of *cislunar* space, the space region between Earth and the moon.

ELECTROMAGNETIC RADIATION

Electromagnetic radiation is the light emitted by the sun, or reflected by the planets or their moons. The sun radiates over a wide range of the SPECTRUM, from infrared through the visible regions into the ultraviolet and far into the X RAY and the still more energetic gamma RADIATION. In space, electromagnetic radiation is the principal factor determining the temperature of a body. In regions far from the sun solar radiation is weak.

The heat input into a space vehicle from solar radiation can be controlled by giving the proper reflectivity to the vehicle's surface. Dark surfaces absorb solar radiation better than white surfaces do. Space vehicles which descend deep into the inner solar system will be given shiny surfaces to reflect as much as possible the overwhelming amount of solar radiation. At the distance of the planet VENUS, the sun's radiation is twice as strong as the radiation at the Earth's distance. A black surface would approach a temperature of 127° F. At the average distance of the planet MERCURY, the radiation is more than six times as strong, causing a black surface to approach 345° F. At this temperature, lead is liquid.

Besides these factors, radiation also determines regions in which life (at least carbon-based life such as that on Earth) has a chance to develop.

For example, on Mercury water could not exist in liquid form even if Mercury were as big as Earth, because the intense solar radiation would make it evaporate. Organic substances would disintegrate in the excessive solid. It is a distinct possibility that lifeforms or simple organic matter presently exist, or once existed, on Jupiter. If so, they evolved in intermediate atmospheric layers where planetary energy, water, carbon dioxide, and nitrogen offered a suitable environment independent of the sun.

CORPUSCULAR RADIATION

Corpuscular radiation consists of high-speed NUCLEAR PARTICLES, mostly electrons, protons, and alpha particles (nuclei of helium atoms). These particles have extremely high speeds, ranging from four million to over four billion miles per hour. Their capability to penetrate matter is far greater than that of the most energetic electromagnetic radiation. This penetration capability and the damage which this radiation can do to living tissue makes it a major problem for manned space flights.

There seem to be two major sources of corpuscular radiation in the solar system: the MILKY WAY and the sun. The radiation coming primarily from the direction of the Milky Way is often referred to as *cosmic* radiation. It appears to be generated in the plane of the galaxy (this plane appears to the observer on Earth as the belt of stars which is called the Milky Way) by vast intragalactic (within the galaxy) magnetic fields. However, cosmic radiation contains the fastest particles ever observed. They easily penetrate the atmosphere and reach far below Earth's surface. They consist not only of protons and alpha particles, but also of nuclei of heavier atoms up to iron. No practical device can shield a space crew from these particles. Fortunately, the intensity is low and appears to be within tolerance limits of the human body, even for prolonged space journeys.

High-energy corpuscular radiation originating in the sun is called a *solar flare*. Solar flares consist primarily of electrons and protons. Their energy is less (about $\frac{1}{10,000}$ of energy of the cosmic radiation) but still quite deadly. Moreover, their DENSITY is higher. For these reasons they represent a greater hazard than the cosmic radiation. Nevertheless, the lower energy of solar flares offers the possibility of at least partial shielding within reasonable technical limits. This increases the weight of a manned spacecraft, particularly on interplanetary missions.

Solar flares seem to be excitation effects in the solar chromosphere and are closely associated with SUNSPOT groups. They appear as a sudden brightening accompanied by a flood of ultraviolet light. They occur quickly (within minutes) and have a lifetime of from 1 to 24 hours. During this period, a stream of high-speed (about four million miles per hour) protons and electrons is discharged into space.

Since solar flares originate primarily in connection with sunspots, their frequency varies with the sunspot cycle (11.5 years). In 1969, just about when the first manned lunar flights were to be undertaken, the sunspot activity was at its peak. Most of the sunspots are observed near the solar equator, up to about 30° latitude. This means that most solar flares will be close to the *ecliptic plane,* the plane in or near which Earth and other planets are located. A spaceship may, therefore, be comparatively safer outside the ecliptic plane than in it. However, interplanetary flight outside the ecliptic plane requires much more energy.

The solar corona expands far into interplanetary space. This expansion, called the *solar wind,* is a stream of less energetic protons and electrons emitted continuously from the sun at velocities ranging from 670,000 to 1.6 million miles per hour.

Charged particles emanating from the sun get trapped in the vicinity of planets which possess a magnetic field. They form radiation belts of the type which have been observed to surround Earth. Earth, for example, is surrounded by two radiation belts of high intensity. The inner belt (mostly protons) reaches a peak intensity at a distance of about 2,000 miles up; the outer belt (mostly electrons) at about 10,000 miles. The intensity of the radiation belt of Jupiter is estimated to be at least a thousand times higher than that of Earth. Instrumented space probes detected no magnetic field near our moon, Venus, or MARS. Consequently, these bodies were found to have no radiation belts.

MAGNETIC FIELDS

Magnetic fields trap particles, causing regions of abnormally high radiation intensity near planets.

MATTER IN SPACE

Matter in space is comprised of meteoritic matter and gases. Micrometeorites (particles the size of a pinhead or smaller) are relatively abundant. They are more frequent on the ecliptic plane than outside it and more abundant near planets than in interplanetary space. They are less numerous inside the Earth's orbit than outside of it. Space probes to Venus have encountered far fewer micrometeorites than have probes to Mars. No space probe is known to have ever encountered larger particles, even though some spacecraft have operated in interplanetary space for years. The larger particles are called meteorites, and they would cause total destruction. Little is as yet known about distribution and abundance of meteoric matter beyond Mars. For general reasons, space in the outer solar system can be more "dusty," especially in the asteroid belt and in the vicinity of the large planets.

Gases are not relevant to flight in the solar system except in the immediate vicinity of planets with atmosphere.

SPACE ENVIRONMENT

Space environment is in many respects favorable to travel. Visibility is excellent. There are no storms, no humidity, and no rot, rust, or bacteria. Unattended space installations will eventually outlast any installation on Earth. People will eventually find it pleasant to live in self-sufficient space facilities. Space will be found to be a preferred environment for many activities, including manufacturing. K. A. E.

SEE ALSO: ASTRONAUTICS, SPACE MEDICINE, SPACE STATION, SPACE TRAVEL

Space medicine Space medicine is the science of keeping flight crews healthy during flight and work in space. Space medicine scientists explore the human body's ability to adjust to short-term or long-term environmental changes and determine the requirements for protection against exposure to harmful conditions. The first half-decade of manned space flight has shown that the human body is far more adaptive and resistant to new environments than it was first thought to be.

Men and women are equally capable of flying and living in space. It has been demonstrated that the human body can, without ill aftereffects, ascend into space at high acceleration and live and do useful work in orbit for a period of two to three weeks. This can be done under conditions of weightlessness and with high-deceleration upon return to the surface. This means that lunar-landing missions are medically feasible. Uncertainties and unknown factors are still associated with space voyages lasting long periods of time, such as months or years. The problems must be taken seriously if tragic accidents are to be avoided and successful manned space flight is to continue. As of 1967, one Russian cosmonaut has lost his life during a space flight mission, according to official Soviet Union reports. The United States lost three astronauts during a ground test of the Apollo lunar flight capsule.

In May, 1958, Air Force Captain E. L. Beeding became the first man to withstand the force of 83G. Note the strained, distorted expression on his face

PHYSIOLOGICAL ASPECTS

Space medicine is concerned with physiological and psychological problem areas. The first area affects the body's behavior, reactions, and adjustments; the second deals with emotional effects.

The physiological aspects of space medicine are numerous, ranging from adjustment of the entire body chemistry to maintenance, equilibrium, vision, and in the long run, dental care. Generally, the physiological aspects can be divided into physiochemical, radiation, and physical aspects. The major concern of space medicine in the physiochemical field is the life support system (LSS) of a spacecraft. Radiation work deals with the long- and short-term effects of particle radiation on tissue cells, blood cells, and reproductive cells of the human body.

Prominent in the physical area are biodynamics and equilibrium. Biodynamics describes the dynamic mechanical properties of living organisms and the effects of force environments on these organisms. For space flight, important characteristics of the force environment are stresses of acceleration (or deceleration), rotation (spin, tumble), vibration (including noise), and reduced or zero gravity (weightlessness).

Another problem of space medicine is ACCELERATION. It tends to increase the apparent weight of the individual in a powered rocket vehicle. Because of the amount of rocket propulsion needed during the ascent to escape the Earth's gravity, astronauts are exposed to accelerations which range from 1.5 to about 7G (1G = 32.2 feet/second^2 = gravitational acceleration of Earth), thus imposing a heavy weight. For example, at 7G the blood is as heavy as liquid iron. Although such conditions put the organism under heavy stress, they are not intolerable. When lying flat on his back facing the direction of acceleration, man can stand considerably higher accelerations, from 20G to 30G, for progressively shorter periods (minutes and finally only seconds). In other positions, man's acceleration tolerance is somewhat lower, but it is usually above 7G. The astronauts in the *Mercury* and *Gemini* capsules lie on their backs with their legs in a slightly elevated position in order to minimize the discomfort resulting from high acceleration. The Apollo astronauts are in the same position during ascent and return.

Rotation, especially motion in a rotating spacecraft, involves many complex cross-correlations of force effects. The purpose of controlled spacecraft rotation (spin or tumble) is to produce an inertial substitute for gravitation (weight). Tests show that a spacecraft or space station should not rotate faster than four revolutions per minute (rpm). The artificial gravity increases with distance from the center. "Down" is away from the spin axis. A person's feet are, therefore, farther away from the spin axis, and gravity is higher on the floor than at eye level. The difference should not exceed 15 percent (that is, an object weighing 1 pound at eye level should not weigh more than 1.15 pounds on the floor). The difference decreases with distance from the spin axis. At 4 rpm, the 15 percent or less value is obtained at a distance to the floor of 45 feet or more.

Suppose a spacecraft has the shape of a tire, with the crew located in the tube. When this spacecraft spins, a person moving in the tube will mostly walk either in the direction the craft is rotating or in the opposite direction. When he walks *with* the rotation, he adds his own speed to that of the rotating system, in effect causing him to rotate faster and become "heavier." If the person is on the 0.85G level, normal walking speed (about 4 feet/second) raises his weight to 1G (Earth level). Conversely, walking against the direction of motion causes reduction in weight. These factors indicate that the gravity level in a rotating spacecraft should not exceed 0.8G.

The gravity level also should not fall below 0.3G. At the 0.15G level or less, a person seems not to be able to walk unaided, at least not without an adjustment period (lunar surface gravity is 0.167G).

Radial movement, such as that between the hub and tube of a tire-shaped spacecraft, causes added cross force (known as the *Coriolis* effect). This is due to the fact that in a spinning rigid system, the speed of rotation, though not the rpm, increases farther from the axis. Suppose the spacecraft rotates clockwise. A person walking from hub to tube through a spoke is pressed against the wall to his left. The opposite occurs in moving from tube to hub. This effect becomes stronger as the person moves faster. Since it

would be inconvenient to restrict radial motion to less than 3 feet/second (on the average), the spacecraft's rpm must be sufficiently low. This requirement results in an upper limit of about 4 rpm up to a distance of about 150 feet. At greater distance, this limit is reduced down to 3 rpm at about 250 feet.

Movement in or against the direction of motion is most frequent if the rotating spacecraft resembles a spinning tire that is cartwheeling with respect to space. The heads of the people living in the tube will point toward the hub when the people are standing. However, for human comfort and highest operating capability, it is more desirable to have people moving primarily at right angles to the spin direction. This is what happens when the spacecraft resembles a ladder, rotating about one rung as the spin axis. The people would live in cylindrical rungs at various distances (gravity levels) from the axis. As people would stand or sit facing the wall of their cylinder (rung), they would spin head over heels. This kind of spin is better for comfort and resistance against motion sickness than is cartwheeling.

Excessive vibration can severely damage body tissue and internal organs. More than being an annoyance, noise can permanently damage a person's balance. Protection against vibration and noise is of primary concern during ascent into space.

Weightlessness is a state of free fall. It is attained after engine shut-off when the spacecraft follows its orbital course freely. Many of the effects of weightlessness on the human body are still not understood. Among the results of prolonged weightlessness as experienced so far are loss of muscle tone and loss of calcium and phosphorus in bones. Hormone balance might also have been changed. The cumulative effects of months or years of weightlessness are especially unknown. No American astronaut and only one Russian cosmonaut, Gherman Titov, became nauseous in flight. Titov suggested that this problem might be peculiar to himself only.

The LSS consists basically of three cycles: atmosphere, liquids, and solids. For short space flights (about thirty days or less) all cycles are open. This means that all consumables to be used on the voyage, such as oxygen, water, and solid foods, are brought into the space vehicle before the flight begins.

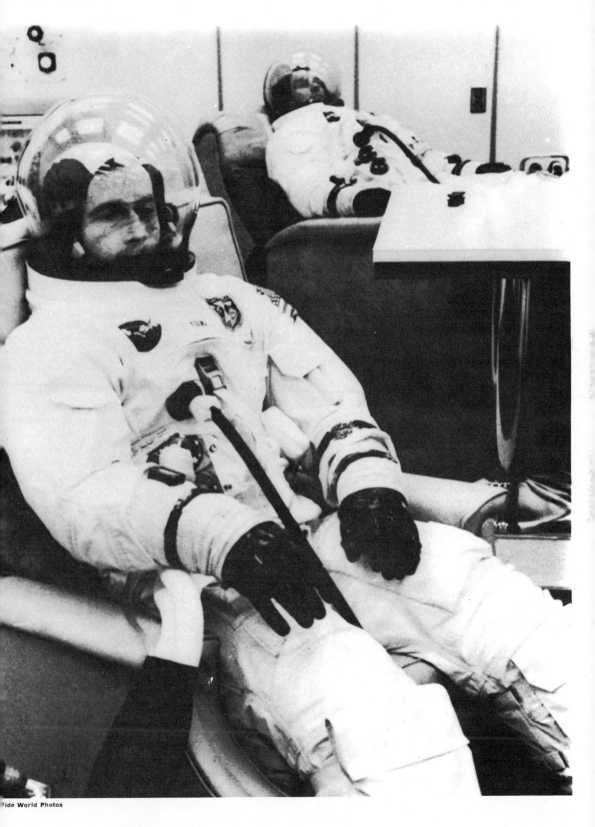

The space suits of Apollo 10 astronauts John Young (front) and Eugene Cernan are checked to verify that all aspects of the life support system are working properly

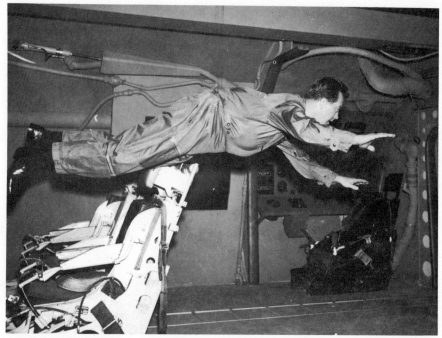

The actor Bill Lundigan gives a demonstration of weightlessness in space. Scientists still do not know for sure what prolonged weightlessness will do to the human body

The waste products, such as carbon dioxide (CO_2) and body eliminations, are dumped overboard. At the end of the voyage, the consumables will virtually be used up.

In order to exist comfortably in his space vehicle, man should have more than the absolute minimum of oxygen, food, and water. The daily requirements of one person are 2 pounds of oxygen, 1.5 pounds of food, and 4.8 pounds of water (58 percent of the water in food and 42 percent in liquid form). This amounts to a total of 8.3 pounds per man per day. This figure does not include the weight of water and other materials such as soap used for hygienic purposes. For longer missions, it pays to convert the waste products back into usable form. This will reduce the total amount of consumables needed at the outset of the voyage, even though the equipment weight will be higher. Regeneration of oxygen from CO_2 and regeneration of water and eventually food from wastes closes the atmospheric, liquid, and solid cycles. When a closed cycle is used, the duration of the space flight can be longer without increasing the weight of the equipment taken on board at the beginning of the flight. There are at least five methods of regenerating oxygen and hydrogen recognized today. A great number of these are still in the planning

stages. Little or no practical use has been made of any regeneration methods for atmosphere. Water used for cleaning and liquid eliminations of the human body through lungs, kidneys, and skin can be reprocessed to such purity that they can be safely reused for human consumption. Reuse of solid waste materials requires an organic processing cycle involving bacteria and low plant life such as duckweed and certain algae. These can either be made suitable for human consumption or, in a larger LSS, can be fed to animals which, in turn, serve human consumption.

Of particular importance is the choice of the proper spacecraft atmosphere. The choice is between pure oxygen and oxygen-nitrogen and oxygen-helium combinations. Each device must be evaluated against physiological, engineering, and fire-blast criteria (Table 1). From the standpoint of engineering requirements (such as equipment, weight, complexity, and ventilation requirements, and sensitivity to longer missions) the pure oxygen atmosphere is most attractive. From the space medical and safety standpoint, oxygen-nitrogen and oxygen-helium mixtures are preferable.

Proper control of temperature and humidity in the spaceship is also of considerable importance. Man's temperature comfort region lies around 70° F.; the humidity comfort region depends on the temperature and ranges from 30 to 70 percent.

If the space cabin springs a leak, the air rapidly escapes into space. The resulting quick drop in cabin pressure is called *sudden decompression* and can be fatal. It was found experimentally that the effects of sudden decompression can be tolerated better when the initial cabin pressure is low. Therefore, the cabin pressure in spaceships will not be 14.7 pounds per square inch (psi) but only 5 to 7 psi (14.7 psi equals 1 atmosphere).

Corpuscular radiation constitutes a serious biological hazard. High-speed electrons may not be able to penetrate the metallic hull of the spacecraft, but they may be powerful enough to produce X radiation (caused by the slowdown of the electrons in the metal). This radiation reaches the interior of the space cabin and converts the space vehicle into a gigantic X ray machine. In order to prevent this, metallic parts must be avoided wherever possible. The crew must be shielded against X rays from metallic walls by lining the walls with a layer of lead capable of absorbing the X rays.

Cosmic radiation which easily penetrates vehicle walls of any practical thickness can produce various kinds of damage to cells which are penetrated by these rays. Fortunately, the cosmic radiation in space appears not to be very dense, so the probability of damage by the limited number of ultra-high energy particles is not large. However, while smashing through the structure of the spaceship, this primary radiation produces a secondary radiation by breaking up atomic nuclei on its way through the structure.

The situation of the crew can be compared to that of people standing behind a glass wall which is under gunfire from the outside. The number of bullets (*primaries*) is much smaller than the number of glass splinters (*secondaries*) flying around. It is probable that more people get hurt by the glass splinters than by the bullets. Imagine now that the glass wall (which symbolizes the spaceship's metal wall) is lined on the inside with rubber. Then essentially only the bullets would penetrate. The rubber liner does not splinter and stops the glass splinters.

In the world of nuclear radiation, metals are known to "splinter" badly, making them very dangerous. Carbon, hydrogen, and water belong to a group of substances which do not splinter, at least not badly. The inner liner, therefore, should consist of HYDROCARBONS (rubber is a very suitable hydrocarbon; other good substances are plastics), of graphite (carbon), or of water or hydrogen. In practice, a one- or two-inch thick inner liner of metal-free rubber or plastic provides adequate protection against secondaries of cosmic radiation.

The high-energy solar flare particles (protons and electrons) must be stopped in the same manner as the secondaries. To do this requires more material due to their higher energy level.

Radiation intensity is measured in *roentgens* (r) or *milliroentgens* (mr), $\frac{1}{1,000}$ of a roentgen. The radiation dose rate is measured in roentgens per hour (r/hr), where 1 r/hr = 1,000 mr/hr. This corresponds to a radiation beam of 7,000 neutrons passing

TABLE I—CORPUSCULAR RADIATION DATA

Normal background radiation in the Earth's atmosphere . . . . .approx. 0.025 milliroentgens/hour	
Maximum acceptable crew dose rate at continuous exposure (for a period of 1-2 years).approx. 1.8 mr/hr	
Cosmic ray flux dose rate (90% protons, 9% alpha particles, 1% heavy nuclei) . . .2.6—5.2 mr/hr	
Maximum known radiation intensity in the Earth's radiation belt . . . . .approx. 100,000 mr/hr (protons)	approx. 10,000 mr/hr (electrons)
Maximum radiation intensity in solar flares estimated to be in excess of . . . . . .approx. 200,000 mr/hr (protons)	approx. 20,000 mr/hr (electrons)
Lethal dose for 10% of normally healthy persons . . . . .approx. 100,000 mr/hr for a period of 3-4 hours	
Dose causing death of 90% of normally healthy persons within 40 days after exposure .approx. 200,000 mr/hr for 3–4 hrs.	
Dose in fall-out area of H-bombs . . . . .approx. 4,000,000 mr/day	

every second at an energy of three million electron volts (3 mev). A neutron or a proton of 3 mev energy moves at a speed of approximately 47 million miles per hour (mph), whereas a 3 mev electron (which weighs about 1/1836 of a neutron or proton) has a speed of about 3 billion mph.

To illustrate the radiation hazard in space, data is presented in Table 1, page 1615. It can be seen that human beings (as well as all organic life) are extremely sensitive to high-energy corpuscular radiation. An unprotected person in the maximum intensity zone of Earth's proton radiation belt would, after only six or eight hours of exposure, face almost certain death within a month.

PSYCHOLOGICAL ASPECTS

Relatively close confinement, a completely artificial way of life, utter dependency upon a very complex system of equipment, forced close association with companions for a long period of time, and the deep loneliness necessarily associated with cosmic separation from the human race and from "the green hills of Earth" may well cause severe psychological stress over extended flight periods. Screening tests have been developed for people who wish to perform jobs with these requirements. Submarine crews, members of Arctic and Antarctic expeditions, and astronauts must all be persons who can tolerate long-duration isolation, extended nights, close togetherness, and the other factors mentioned above. More men than women have been tested. Men have been found to vary widely in their ability to withstand the STRESS of long confinement. However, women indicate, in general, an average superiority over men in their capability to withstand the irritations of daily life under such conditions. However, most experience has been collected on Earth. For their selection and training it is necessary to subject potential crews to long-duration conditions similar to those that they will experience on their project.   K. A. E.

SEE ALSO: ASTRONAUT, WEIGHTLESSNESS

Apollo 12 astronaut Alan Bean shaves his beard as Pete Conrad watches. Physical closeness imposed by space travel is one of the many problems studied in the field of space medicine

NASA

TABLE I—PROBABLE CREW COMPOSITION FOR INTERPLANETARY FLIGHTS

PROFESSION	SPECIALIZATION	PRIMARY PROFESSIONAL RESPONSIBILITY	ORGANIZATIONAL RESPONSIBILITY
Pilot and Engineer	Mechanical and Nuclear	Overall vehicle system, propulsion	Command of space vehicle
Pilot and Engineer	Electronics	Guidance, control, navigation on board electronic computer system	First deputy commander
Pilot and Engineer	Electrical and Nuclear	All electrical systems, cable system, converters, generators, auxiliary power supply	Second deputy commander
Pilot and Engineer	Nuclear	Propulsion specialist	Specialist
Pilot and Engineer	Mechanical	All mechanical subsystems	Specialist
Pilot and Engineer	Electronics	Instrumentation communication, robot systems	Specialist
Pilot and Physician	Medicine Dentistry Psychiatry Radiology Biology Medical technology	Biotechnical life support systems, food and sanitary control, health and morale of the crew	Medical officer

Space pilot A space pilot is an ASTRONAUT trained in piloting a spacecraft or lander. The mission commander is in charge of the spacecraft and execution of its mission. He directs the operations of the crew.

The Apollo crew consists of commander, command module pilot, and lunar module pilot. Flight training is important for all crew members. During exploration flights to the MOON and to other planets, everyone on board must be equally well prepared to operate the entire spacecraft, both in the normal flight operations and in emergency situations. But to an increasing degree, there will be emphasis on the scientific objectives of future manned flights to the moon and the planets. Table 1 describes the kinds of things which crews flying to other planets will have to do. It is therefore necessary to provide competent observers who can successfully accomplish the scientific objectives of the flights.

Preflight training of Apollo astronauts concentrates on three areas—academics, flight operations, and survival. Table 2 shows the considerable extent of preflight training

TABLE 2—PREFLIGHT TRAINING OF APOLLO ASTRONAUTS

Academic	Survival	Flight Operations
Geology Field Trips (4) Mineralogy and Petrology Vulcanism Impact Geology } (103 hrs)	Training for Survival on Water, in Desert or in Jungle Instructions on how to Live off the Land or to Survive in Capsule on the Water	Flight Simulator Training Launch Vehicle Characteristics Spacecraft Characteristics Failure Modes Abort Systems
Flight Mechanics (40 hrs)		Docking Simulator Training for Docking Maneuvers in Orbit
Astronomy (15 hrs)		Mission Procedures Development
Digital Computers (12 hrs)		
On-Board Gemini IBM System (24 hrs)		High-g Acceleration Testing in Centrifuge
Propulsion (12 hrs)		Lunar Excursion Simulator Training
Aerodynamics (10 hrs)		
Physics of Upper Atmosphere and Earth Space (12 hrs)		Weightlessness Training Aboard USAF/Boeing KC-135 Flying Parabolas which Produce 15-25 sec of Weightlessness
Guidance and Navigation (34 hrs)		
Communications (4 hrs)		Practice in Helicopters in Hovering and Descent
Meteorology (4 hrs)		
Medical Aspects (12 hrs)		
Gemini and Apollo Systems		

of the Apollo astronauts in each of these areas. The emphasis on academic subjects maximizes their usefulness on the lunar surface. Selection of a crew for a specific mission is normally done six months before the flight. The crew and its backup then begin an intensive training schedule that includes not only training in the overall mission objectives and experiments but also a refresher course in many of the fields already covered during earlier instruction.

Future crew sizes depend on the size of the spaceship, type of propulsion system, and duration of the mission. For missions to Venus and Mars the crew size will be from six to a preferred twelve persons.   K. A. E.

SEE ALSO: SPACE, SPACE TRAVEL, SPACE VEHICLES

Top: Apollo 12 astronauts Richard Gordon (left) and Alan Bean talk to suiting personnel before their flight to the moon. Bottom: Apollo 12 commander Charles Conrad, Jr., has his suit checked just prior to the launch   Both, NASA

Space station A space station is an artificial satellite on which man can live. It is different from its forerunners, the *Mercury* and *Gemini* capsules, in that it is "permanent." It will stay in orbit without possibility of re-entry into Earth's atmosphere, which would destroy it. Man will live on it for short periods of time. His supplies and travel to and from, as well as his communications, would require a dependable Earth-to-orbit (ETO) supply and travel system. Even a small space station can accommodate three or more persons.

The inhabitable space station will be one of the most important tools of the astronautical engineer and the scientist. Many experiments and astronomical observations are only possible in space and not on the Earth's surface. This is because of low or zero weight and absence of atmospheric interference.

Among the variety of uses of the orbiting laboratory are: (1) To serve as a laboratory for the development and testing of life support equipment for long-duration flight, instrumentation, spaceship components and subsystems to be used in lunar and inter-planetary space vehicles. (2) It can serve as a laboratory for the selection and training of crews for space vehicles with long-duration missions, either in space stations or lunar and interplanetary space vehicles. (3) It can be useful in developing and perfecting ETO operations, such as orbital meetings, docking, space crew rotation, etc. Ability in this field is a prerequisite for manned deep space missions. (4) A space station can serve as a simulator for conditioning space crews to special extended space missions in life support systems which are a close or accurate duplication of their mission life support system. This includes, among other things, training for emergencies, or living on the lunar gravity level (1/6 of the earth's) in preparation of lunar landings or assignments to a lunar base. (5) And it can serve as a space biological laboratory for conducting various experiments at zero or low gravity levels.

Space flight simulation is important because the selection and flight training of space crews on the ground is severely handicapped. Weightlessness cannot be simulated for adequate periods of time, and it is not possible to duplicate the psychological effects of prolonged space flight. These two factors, however, are important in determining the final qualifications of space crew members. The mental attitude, the efficiency, the endurance, and the degree of teamwork of the crew members are intimately connected with their long-term response, both psychologically and physiologically, to life in space. In order to determine their response with any finality, crew members must spend days, weeks, or even months in an orbital test bed.

K. A. E.

SEE ALSO: ASTRONAUTICS, SPACE MEDICINE, SPACE TRAVEL, SPACE VEHICLE

Space travel Space travel is manned flight from one celestial body to another. Space travel, like air travel, is a matter of: (1) propulsion (the force to go), (2) navigation (knowledge of the way to go), and (3) adaptation (the ability to live in an artificial environment). A manned spacecraft must provide life support, some comfort, and a means of exercise during longer missions in order to preserve physical fitness and mental alertness.

Propulsion is vital because the travel time through space depends entirely on the energy of the vehicle's propulsion system. Navigation implies the ability of determining one's position in space, the orbit of the spaceship, and correction maneuvers, if needed.

Space travel begins with the ascent from a surface into an orbit. It may end right there if the destination is a space station in a near-Earth orbit (about 250 miles altitude).

Space travel to the moon begins in an Earth orbit. The spacecraft is injected into a transfer orbit through cislunar space (space between the Earth and the moon). Near the moon, a *capture* maneuver causes the spacecraft to be captured in the lunar gravity field. This turns its path into a circumlunar orbit. Once the proper orbit is established, a Lunar Module (LM) separates from the spacecraft and descends to the surface. Its occupants perform their assigned tasks and then the LM ascends, performs its rendezvous, and docks with the orbiting spacecraft. The lunar astronauts board the orbiting spacecraft and jettison the LM. The spacecraft then leaves its circumlunar orbit and is injected into a return transfer path to Earth (trans-Earth trajectory). For the Apollo missions, not enough propulsion energy is available to break the space vehicle into an Earth orbit. The Apollo

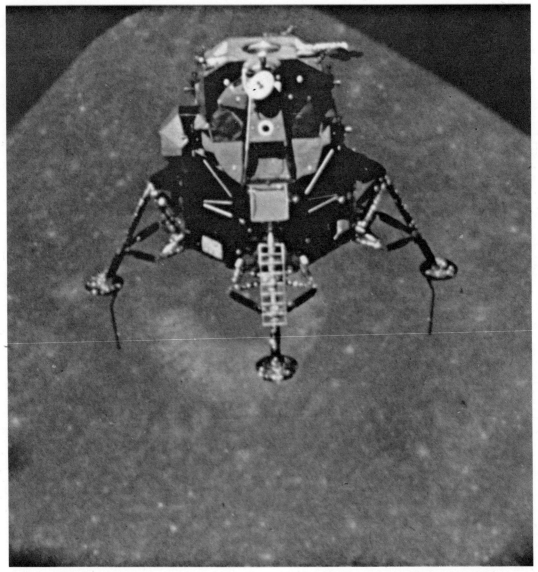

NASA

The Apollo 12 Lunar Module, separated from the Command Module, prepares to descend to the surface of the moon. The Lunar Module, carrying Astronauts Conrad and Bean, successfully landed in the Sea of Storms in November, 1969.

NASA

A full view of the Lunar Module on the moon. One of the astronauts is at the work station

three-man Command Module (CM) uses the Earth's atmosphere to reduce its arrival speed of 25,000 miles per hour (mph) to a speed low enough to release a parachute system. This parachute system lets the CM gently descend to a water landing. Future, more advanced cislunar transports will "shuttle" back and forth between Earth and circumlunar orbit. Passengers from Earth or the moon will change spacecraft at both terminals.

The travel time from Earth to other planets depends greatly on the *speed of transfer* (the length of time it takes to get from the Earth orbit to the orbit of the target body). On arrival in the new orbit, the spaceship will next have to land on the target planet. The target planet, therefore, cannot just simply be anywhere in its orbit when the space-

craft leaves Earth. The time .of the spacecraft's lift-off from the terminal is directly related to the position of the target planet.

Spacecraft are only able to travel to other planets at specific times during the year. These times occur whenever the target planet is in the proper position in its orbit for the landing of a spacecraft.

The orbit the spacecraft must take is called a *hyperbolic* orbit, because of its shape. The opportunity for transfer is called a *launch window*. A launch window to other planets usually lasts from one to two months.

If the orbits of the planets were circular and lay in the same plane, it would be possible to use a transfer orbit that has the shape of a half ellipse, tangential to the orbits of Earth and the target planet.

TABLE 1 A- TRAVEL TIMES FROM EARTH TO ALL PLANETS OF THE SOLAR SYSTEM FOR SIMPLE TANGENT TRANSFER ORBIT

Planets	Travel Time to Target Planet	Orbital Capture Period	Travel Time to Earth	Total Travel Time
Earth-Mercury-Earth	105.5 days	67 days	105.5 days	278 days
Earth-Venus-Earth	146 days	468 days	146 days	2.08 years
Earth-Mars-Earth	258.8 days	455 days	258.8 days	2.66 years
Earth-Jupiter-Earth	2.73 years	214 days	2.73 years	6.04 years
Earth-Saturn-Earth	6.05 years	341 days	6.05 years	13.03 years
Earth-Uranus-Earth	16.03 years	346 days	16.03 years	33 years
Earth-Neptune-Earth	30.6 years	292 days	30.6 years	62 years
Earth-Pluto-Earth	45.6 years	291 days	45.6 years	92 years

Table 1 A shows three basic facts: (1) the travel time to and from the target planet is the same because the same transfer orbit is taken; (2) the transfer periods, and therefore the total travel times, get very long if planets of the outer solar system are considered, eventually reaching the time of the human life-span; (3) the orbital capture periods are fairly long in all cases, but especially long in the case of Venus and Mars.

The reason for the capture periods is that the spaceship must wait until the correct planet formation for meeting Earth on the return flight is again established. The particularly long duration of the capture periods near Venus and Mars is caused by the fact that the orbital velocities of these two planets are not too different in comparison with that of Earth. This means they move relatively slowly with respect to each other. This small difference causes the long waiting times for a particular constellation. Since the planetary orbits are slightly elliptic and are not located in exactly the same plane, the actual mission times differ somewhat from those shown in Table 1 A.

Obviously, most of the travel times indicated in Table 1 A are unacceptable for manned space flight. There exist "faster" trajectories if enough propulsion energy is available to fly them. A typical example of very fast round-trip mission profiles to Venus and Mars is shown above. The total travel time is indicated by the angle through which Earth has traveled between departure and return of the spacecraft. Thus the Mars round-trip mission still requires about nine months even along

these very-high-energy transfer paths; the Venus round trip takes about eight months in the example shown. The first round trips to other planets will be a matter of one to several years. The first missions to Venus and Mars are likely to require at least 1 and 1.5 years, respectively.   K. A. E.

SEE ALSO: ASTRONAUTICS, SPACE MEDICINE, SPACE STATION, SPACE VEHICLES, WEIGHTLESSNESS

Space vehicles Space vehicles are self-propelled devices (supplying their own power) that are designed to operate in space (outside an atmosphere) as well as within an atmosphere.

There are four main groups of space vehicles (Table 1): Earth launch vehicles (ELV), orbiting space vehicles (OSV), interorbital space vehicles (ISV), and descent and landing vehicles (DLV). Of these, the ELV, ISV, and DLV represent primarily a means of transportation from surface to space, between points in space, and from space to surface, respectively. Not all of the vehicles listed in Table 1 have been built and flown so far. Some are still in the planning stage.

The first decade of the Space Age ended in October, 1967. During this

TABLE 1   CLASSIFICATION OF SPACE VEHICLES

	General Specifications	Destination	Manned (M) Unmanned (U)	Propulsion	Reusable?
• Earth Launch Vehicles					
* Ballistic Type (small to heavy loads)	Small Carriers	Earth Orbit	U	Chemical	No
	Thor Family	Earth Orbit	U	Chemical	No
	Atlas Family	Earth Orbit	U	Chemical	No
	Titan Family	Earth Orbit	U(M)#	Chemical	No
	Saturn Family	Earth Orbit	U/M	Chemical	No
	Post-Saturn	Earth Orbit	U/M	Chemical	Yes
* Ballistic or Winged (passengers and/or Small loads)	Orbital Shuttle Transport	Earth Orbit	M	Chemical or Nuclear	Yes
• Orbiting Space Vehicles	Satellites	Earth Orbit	U	Only auxiliary propulsion for control and station keeping+	Operating life to increase to years and decades in the next 20 years
	Orbiters	Moon, Planets	U		
	Orbiting Lab.	Earth Orbit	M*		
	Space Stations	Earth, Sun, Planets	M*		
• Interorbital Space Vehicles	Cislunar	Moon	M	Chemical or Nuclear	Eventually
	Heliocentric	Planets	M		Eventually
	Bus (Space Probe)	Moon, Planets	U		No
• Descent and Landing Vehicles	Reentry Vehicles	Earth	M	—	Eventually
	Lander	Moon, Planets	U	Chemical	No
	Landing Vehicle	Moon, Planets	M	Chemical	Eventually

*May be man-attended, that is, not necessarily inhabited continuously.

+Station keeping means to maintain the vehicle's orbit and its position (not its attitude; attitude control is a separate task) in that orbit.

#Titan III can be used as manned orbital transport, but present (1969) versions are equipped for unmanned launchings only.

TABLE 2   EARTH LAUNCH VEHICLES: BALLISTIC TYPE

Launch Vehicle	Stage	Propellant	Thrust (lb.)	Payload (lb.) Orbit 150 n. mi.	Escape	Transportation Cost ($/lb. Payload) Orbit	Escape	Payload
Scout (improved version)	1	Solid	1 @ 100,900					Small
	2	Solid	1 @ 60,500					Research
	3	Solid	1 @ 22,600					Satellites
	4	Solid	1 @ 5,900	320	—	4,400	—	
Delta	1 (Thor)	LO₂/RP	170,000					Small
	2 (Delta)	IRFNA/UDMH	7,800	1,200	100	2,600	31,000	Research Satellites
TAID [Thrust Augmented (Thor) Improved Delta] (TAT = Thrust Augmented Thor)	1 (TAT)	LO₂/RP (Main Engine)	170,000					Satellites Inter-planetary
		Solid (2 Strap-ons)	163,500					Probes
	2 (Delta)	IRFNA/UDMH	1 @ 7,800	1,930	550	1,800	6,000	(Pioneer)
TAT-Agena D (TAT = Thrust Augmented Thor)	1 (TAT)	LO₂/RP (Main Engine)	170,000					Research and Weather
	2 (Ag-D)	Solid (Strap-ons)	163,500					Satellites
		IRFNA/UDMH	16,000	1,750	—	3,500	—	
Atlas-Agena D (SLV-3A)	1½	LO₂/RP	360,000 to 390,000					Mariner to Venus, Mars
		IRFNA/UDMH	1 @ 16,000	6,900	1,200	1,000	5,000	Lunar Orbiter Satellites
Atlas-Centaur (SLV-3C)	1½	LO₂/RP	360,000					Mariner (Mars, 1969, 1971)
	2	LO₂/LH₂	2 @ 15,000	11,500	2,900	1,000	4,000	
								Surveyor Moon Lander OAO Large Satel. Small Ju. Probes (1972-84). Elec. Interpl. Space Probe (70's)
Titan IIIA (St. 3 referred to as Transtage)	1	N₂O₄/(N₂H₄/UDMH)	2 @ 235,000					Defense
	2	N₂O₄/(N₂H₄/UDMH)	1 @ 100,000					Satellite
	3	N₂O₄/(N₂H₄/UDMH)	2 @ 8,000	6,200	—	9,000	—	Programs

The Atlas Agena launch vehicle lifts off from its pad at Cape Kennedy

period, a great variety of ELVs was used. Of the small carriers, only the Scout is still in use and likely to remain so for an indefinite period. Over the years, ELV performance (bringing the payload into orbit) increased as more efficient upper stages (as in the Centaur), or strap-on solid rockets (Titan III), or bigger boosters (Saturn 1B, Saturn V) were developed. After 1964, launch vehicles were increasingly standardized in order to reduce cost. Table 2 presents characteristic data of ballistic-type ELVs in use in 1969 and planned for use in the 1970s.

In the column "Thrust," the number of engines and the thrust per engine are shown. In the Atlas, the effect of altitude on engine thrust must be considered. Lift-off occurs with three engines. Two engines at 150,000-pound thrust each are dropped during flight (first and second stages), and the vehicle continues on the remaining (sustainer) engine. At lift-off, this engine has a 60,000-pound thrust. Under near-vacuum conditions at altitude, the thrust is increased to 90,000 pounds. Although there exists a large number of propellant (oxidizer fuel) combinations, the launch vehicles are standardized to a very small number for reasons of economy.

In the column "Payload," the load is listed which the ELV can carry into an orbit approximately 150 nautical

The Atlas Centaur launch vehicle shown here is used for deep space probes, planetary flybys, and soft spacecraft landings

SPACE VEHICLE TERMS

COMET (artificial) — An instrumented space vehicle moving about the sun in a highly eccentric orbit which leads far into the outer solar system or beyond the planet Pluto and whose orbit plane may deviate more or less from the ecliptic plane (plane of the Earth orbit).

DRAG BODY—A blunt entry body with little or no lift, producing essentially from drag; must land on a parachute.

ENTRY CAPSULE (Atmospheric)—An encapsuled instrument package designed for atmospheric entry from an orbit.

ENTRY GLIDER—Streamlined entry body, producing more lift than drag, designed for good aerodynamic qualities during subsonic flight and landing.

ENTRY VEHICLE (Atmospheric)—A space vehicle (manned or non-manned) which is capable of entering the atmosphere of a planet at orbital speed.

LIFT-DRAG BODY—Stubby entry body, capable of producing a significant amount of lift and drag due to lift (rather than due to bluntness alone) during atmospheric entry; may have to land on a parachute.

OAO—Orbital Astronautical Observatory, an instrumented Earth satellite for carrying out astronautical observations outside the disturbing atmosphere.

OGO—Orbital Geophysical Observatory, an instrumented Earth satellite for geophysical observations.

PLANETOID (artificial) —An instrumented space vehicle moving about the sun in a more or less stationary orbit of low or moderate eccentricity.

SATELLITE (artificial)—A space vehicle (manned or non-manned) moving in a more or less stationary orbit about a planet or a moon.

SATELLOID—An orbital vehicle (manned or non-manned) moving in the outer regions of an atmosphere, thereby requiring a small amount of thrust to sustain the orbit against the weak atmospheric drag force which tends to slow the satelloid down.

SOLAR MONITOR—A planetoid whose orbit is close to the Sun for the purpose of studying the Sun and detecting solar flares before they endanger manned space vehicles operating in Venus-Mars space or beyond.

SPACE BOAT—A small manned space ship used for auxiliary or emergency purposes; for instance, for commuting between large ships of an interplanetary fleet, for limited excursion missions from the mother ship, for repair work and for emergency maneuvers if the ship is paralyzed by excessive damage.

SPACE BOOSTER—High-thrust vehicle used to boost payloads from the Earth surface into orbit. Sometimes used to designate the first stage of an Earth-to-orbit vehicle (see Space Carrier).

SPACE CAPSULE—(1) A small encapsuled instrument package which can be separated from the spacecraft or spaceship; (2) a small manned space vehicle, essentially a cockpit, such as the Russian space capsule Vostov, the U. S. space capsule Mercury (1-man) or Gemini (2-men); (3) maneuverable capsules containing a crew of one or several persons engaged in orbital assembly or fueling work.

SPACE CARRIER—Synonymous to Space Booster if the latter term is used to designate all stages of a multi-stage Earth-to-orbit vehicle.

SPACE VEHICLE—Any non-stationary vehicle system operating in orbit and/or ascending from or descending to the surface of a celestial body.

SPACECRAFT—Instrumented space vehicle used for lunar and planetary reconnaissance and exploration.

SPACESHIP—Large interorbital space vehicle, used for flights to the Moon and to the planets. May be manned or non-manned (cargo ship).

miles high, or 173 land miles, (*parking orbit*); also listed is the load which can be injected into a *parabolic orbit*. This orbit requires the lowest possible speed at which an object can escape forever from the Earth's gravity field. Injection into a transfer orbit to the moon requires almost parabolic speed (about 25,200 mph). In order to reach planets, the escaping body must follow a *hyperbolic orbit*. The injection velocities in this case are upward of 26,000 mph.

It can be seen that the cost of transporting one pound of payload into space is very high. This is so because the ELV is not recoverable and, therefore, can be used only once. The situation is comparable to discarding a jet airliner after it has made one flight from New York to Los Angeles. This would be intolerable economically. Therefore, an ELV must be developed that is recoverable and can be reused many times (100 to 1,000 times) to reduce transportation costs to between $1 and $10 per pound of payload delivered.

There are two ways to make a reusable ELV. It can be done either by using blunt-body configurations (remotely resembling an *Apollo* or *Gemini* capsule, only larger) or by adopting a lifting configuration. The latter is only suitable for smaller launch vehicles or for the first stage of large ELVs. The blunt-body configuration is suitable for either small or large ELVs. The development of either configuration is very costly (several billion dollars) and therefore not worthwhile until there is a much greater number of launchings than is carried out at present. Major investment into a fully reusable ELV will be delayed until a sufficiently large Earth-to-orbit

This Saturn space vehicle is undergoing a countdown demonstration test on its launch pad
NASA

transportation "market" has evolved. This may not be the case before the 1980s. The development of such a vehicle, however, requires a lead time of at least eight years and should be planned for the 1970s.

The Scout is an all-solid-propelled four-stage "economy launch vehicle." Even though the cost-per-pound-payload is high, the launch cost is lower than that of any other ELV. The principal boosters in use now are the Thor, the TAT (using solid strap-ons), the Atlas, and the Titan III. Important upper stages are the Delta, Agena-D, and Centaur (in order of increasing size and performance). The Agena, of which there were formerly several versions, has been standardized to the Agena-D. It uses inhibited white fuming nitric acid and unsymmetrical dimethyl hydrazine. The Atlas has been standardized to two launch vehicles. These are SLV-3A, with the Agena as upper stage, and SLV-3C with the Centaur, the first vehicle to use liquid hydrogen and the most powerful of the upper stages presently in operation. The Atlas SLV family is derived from the Atlas ICBM which also carried the *Mercury* one-man spacecraft. The Titan III family is derived from the ICBM Titan II, which was also used as carrier for the Gemini two-man spacecraft.

The largest United States launch vehicle, the Saturn V, is an entirely new development. The first stage, S-IC, is powered by five of the largest liquid-propellant engines ever built in the United States, each producing a thrust of 1.5 million pounds. The power output of each engine corresponds to about 92,000 megawatts each second of its burning time. In 1959, the annual power consumption in the entire United States was 11.3 million megawatt hours, corresponding to an average power consumption of 3,140 megawatts during each second of the year. The power output of one engine of Saturn V's stage one is seen to be about 30 times this amount. The second stage of Saturn V is the largest oxygen-hydrogen-powered rocket stage ever developed. The third stage constitutes the second-largest oxygen-hydrogen vehicle developed (following Centaur), dubbed S-IVB because in one earlier design it served as the fourth stage. In flights on their way to an orbit, only the first and second stages are required to deliver the S-IVB and its payload into orbit. In Apollo moon flights, the S-IVB injects the spacecraft into a transfer orbit to the moon.

ORBITING SPACE VEHICLES (OSV)

The family of orbiting space vehicles may be divided into satellites, orbiters and orbiting laboratories, and space stations. Orbiting space vehicles are essentially stationary, as far as the space region in which they operate is concerned.

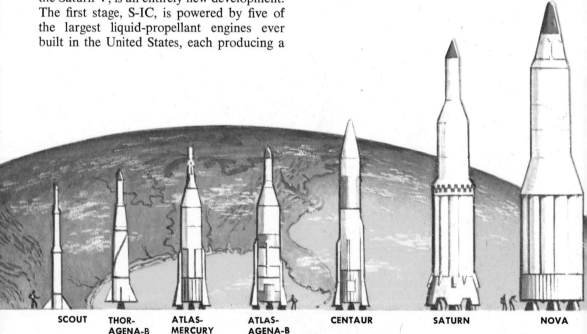

| SCOUT | THOR-AGENA-B | ATLAS-MERCURY | ATLAS-AGENA-B | CENTAUR | SATURN | NOVA |

LAUNCH VEHICLES

TABLE 3 ORBITING SPACE VEHICLES: SOME EARTH SATELLITES

Satellite	Designation	Mission
Scientific Satellites	Biosatellite	Satellite containing 3 returning capsules for 3-, 21- and 30-day biological experiments to study effects of weightlessness and radiation
	Explorer	Research program involving a variety of small satellites in near-Earth to highly elliptical orbits for physical, geophysical, space physical, and astronomical experiments
	OAO	Orbiting Astronomical Observatory for telescopic observations from a precisely stabilized platform outside the Earth's atmosphere
	OGO	Orbiting Geophysical Observatory carrying experiments for the study of interactions between Sun, Earth, and space environment
	OSO	Orbiting Solar Observatory. As OAO, but for solar observations
Technology Satellites	ATS	Applications Technology Satellite for testing advanced components for future communication, navigation, and meteorological satellites
	ERS	Environmental Research Satellite. A series of small satellites carrying a variety of scientific and engineering experiments
	OV	Orbiting Vehicle. A series of low-cost satellites in support of various scientific and engineering space technological research efforts
Application Satellites	ERSAT	Earth Resources Satellite carrying optical, infrared, and ultraviolet sensors to acquire data relating to oceanography, geology, hydrology, agriculture, and forestry
	Intelsat I	Early Bird. First generation commercial communications satellite. Stationed over the Atlantic. One TV channel or 240 two-way voice channels
	Intelsat II	Lani Bird. Second generation commercial COMSAT, located over Atlantic and Pacific. Primary objective is support of Apollo program communications
Application Satellites	Intelsat III	Global COMSAT. Third generation commercial COMSAT for a full global system. Four TV channels or 1200 two-way voice channels
	Nimbus	Second generation experimental satellite for testing new sensors and subsystems. Satellite carries advanced vidicon cameras, an automatic picture transmission system and radiometers to provide nighttime cloud cover photographs. Moves in 22,000-mile-high near-polar orbit viewing each area of Earth twice daily
	Tiros	Television and Infra-Red Observation Satellite. First generation experimental weather satellite. The series consisting of 8 satellites returned over 300,000 cloud cover photographs
	TOS (ESSA=Environmental Science Services Administration)	Tiros Operational Satellite. Standard configuration carries two cameras. Some carry infrared radiometer sensors for nighttime cloud measurements. A pair of TOS serves as operational weather satellite system, named ESSA after successful polar orbit establishment. The first pair, ESSA 1, was orbited in the first half of 1966

TABLE 4   ORBITING SPACE VEHICLES: ORBITERS

Orbiter	Designation	Mission
Moon Orbiting Probe	Lunar Orbiter	Program objectives are to map the near and far side of the Moon for the primary purpose of obtaining topographic data in the lunar equatorial region, from 43°E to 56°W, for assisting in the selection of Apollo lunar landing sites. Also, gravitation, micrometeoroid, and radiation data are gathered. Program consisted of 5 Lunar Orbiters launched in 1966/67. Spacecraft weighs 850 lb. Solar cells and nickel-cadmium batteries provided about 375 watts of power. Photos of almost the entire lunar surface down to less than a few feet resolution were obtained. Orbiter photographed Moon from over 18,000 miles down to about 20 miles altitude.
Mars Orbiter	Viking Mars Orbiter (and Lander; see Mars Lander)	Viking is a projected Mars probe whose purpose it is to orbit and map Mars and deliver a Lander to the surface. Program objective is to gain planetary data, search for life, and collect data related to the origin of the solar system. The first Viking is planned for 1975.
Venus Orbiter	Voyager Venus Orbiter	Spaceprobe possibly of the Mariner type to orbit Venus and map its surface by means of radar waves to penetrate the thick cloud layer covering the planet's surface. No plans have been made for a Venus orbiter in the early seventies.
Solar Orbiters	Pioneer	Deep space probe placed in solar orbit inside and outside the Earth's orbit (between Venus and Mars) to collect data on interplanetary magnetic fields, the solar wind, solar flares, and cosmic radiation. Modified Pioneer probes will be launched to Jupiter in 1972 and 1973.
	Solar Probe (Helios)	Small spacecraft intended to approach Sun as close as 0.3 astronomical units (about Mercury distance) to collect and transmit similar data as gathered by Pioneer. Project is in the planning stage for flights in 1974/75.

The term *satellite* designates unmanned instrumented spacecraft orbiting Earth. Table 3 shows a representative list of the United States' satellites, consisting of three major groups: scientific, technology, and application satellites. The scientific satellites may be viewed as small automated research laboratories that were put into orbit to utilize the vacuum and weightlessness available in space. The technology satellites serve as test beds for the engineering development of subsystems and components to be used later in operational space vehicles. The application satellites are designed to utilize the particular environmental characteristics of space and orbits (vacuum, altitude, rapid Earth circumnavigation, and good observational possibilities when looking down from outside the atmosphere as compared to looking up from the bottom of the atmosphere).

Space satellites have a great variety of unconventional shapes. One of the reasons for this is that *solar cells* are used as the source of electric power. These solar cells may be attached to the body of the satellite or be arranged in panels of various sizes and shapes.

Unmanned spacecraft turned satellites of the moon or planets are called *orbiters*. Table 4 shows lunar, planetary, and solar orbiters presently in use or in the advanced planning stage. The lunar orbiter program was carried out in 1966-67 with complete success. Many tens of thousands of photographs of the lunar surface were returned.

Extraordinary pictures were returned by Mars flyby probes in 1964 and 1969. But only an orbiter can map a planet completely. The first Mars orbiter will circle Mars in 1971-72. Later, improved orbiters will be dis-

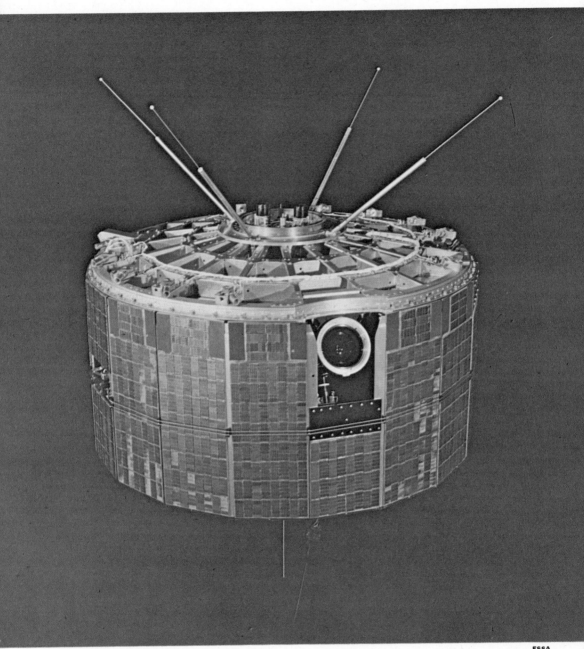

ESSA

This is one of the *Tiros* (Television and Infra-Red Observation Satellite) series of satellites. They were the earliest experimental weather satellites. They sent back more than 300,000 photographs of the earth's cloud cover

patched there in 1973 and 1975 as part of the Viking program. Solar orbiters circle the sun like tiny planets. Pioneer probes have been inserted into *heliocentric* orbits (orbits around the sun) between Earth and Venus and into orbits between Earth and Mars. Their mission objective is the exploration of the magnetic, radiative, and micrometeoritic conditions in these respective space regions. Eventually similar probes will be sent very close to the sun (solar probe), into the asteroid belt, and out of the plane of the ecliptic (the plane in which most of the planets are located).

The third branch of the OSV family comprises manned orbiting space vehicles. At the present level of space technology, these are restricted to Earth-orbiting vehicles, although a temporary manned lunar orbiting laboratory is likely to be realized in the early 1970s. The manned orbiting vehicles flown so far by the United States are in the Mercury, Gemini, and Apollo projects. Orbiting laboratories and space stations that are to follow in the 1970s are surveyed in Table 5.

INTERORBITAL SPACE VEHICLES (ISV)

The ISV is not designed to enter an atmosphere or to land on the surface of another body. A reentry vehicle or landing vehicle may, during transit, fulfill the role or be a part of an ISV system. There are two major kinds of ISV—the unmanned version, referred to as Bus, and the manned spacecraft. Within the latter branch are the Cislunar Interorbital Space Vehicle (CISV) for manned transportation between Earth and moon, and the Heliocentric ISV (HISV) for manned transportation between Earth and other planets. ISVs are surveyed in Table 6.

The purpose of the Bus is to carry a set of instruments (science payload) to where the measurements are to be conducted. Often, the Bus becomes an orbiter (as in the Viking) at its destination. In the Apollo mission, the Lunar Module (LM) is carried by, but is not a functional part of, the Apollo CISV (the Command and Service Module). This is because the LM is used or activated only for descent to the lunar surface and ascent to the orbiting spacecraft. After performing these functions, it is discarded. The LM is part of the transportation payload of the

CISV rather than an integral operating part of the CISV itself.

DESCENT AND LANDING VEHICLES (DLV)

The DLV family consists of manned space vehicles surveyed in Table 7. Mercury and Gemini are also being used as temporary experimental orbiting space vehicles. They are provided with a small retro-rocket propulsion system for deorbiting and descent. They are also with a shape and heat-shield protection. It allows them to reenter the atmosphere at 17,500 mph. In the case of the Apollo spacecraft, the Command Module (CM) is designed for reentry into the atmosphere for a different reason, namely, to eliminate the need for the propellant that otherwise would have to be used up before the CM could return into an Earth orbit at the end of the mission. This propellant, enough to slow the CM down by about 10,000 feet/second, would have to be carried throughout the lunar journey. This would greatly increase the initial orbiting departure mass to a value far above the carrying capability of Saturn V. Thus, it would become necessary to carry the load up in two or three Saturn V launch vehicles and to assemble these loads in orbit prior to injection into the cislunar transfer orbit. All this would make the initial manned lunar missions considerably more costly and complex. For the same reasons (cost and orbital departure weight), it is more advantageous to use a separate landing vehicle (Lunar Module) instead of landing an entire spacecraft on the moon.

The only unmanned vehicle in the United States' space program to have landed softly on another celestial body is the lunar lander named the Surveyor. Plans are in progress to develop a Mars lander. Project Viking is scheduled for the first soft landing on Mars in 1973. **K. A. E.**

SEE ALSO: ASTRONAUTICS, SPACE STATION, SPACE TRAVEL, WEIGHTLESSNESS

(The rapid developments in both the United States and the Soviet Union prevent a completely up-to-date reporting of space technology. Further information will be available in supplementary volumes of this encyclopedia.)

TABLE 5 ORBITING SPACE VEHICLES: ORBITING LABORATORIES AND SPACE STATIONS

Manned Orbiting Vehicle	Designation	Mission
1-Man Spacecraft	Mercury Spacecraft weight in orbit about 3000 lb. Max. dia: 5.9 ft. Length: 8.95 ft.	First part of a 3-part manned space flight program by NASA. The first sub-orbital flight was carried out on April 23, 1961. The first orbital flight (1 orbit) was completed successfully on February 20, 1962. The last flight took place on May 15, 1963.
2-Man Spacecraft	Gemini Spacecraft weight in orbit about 8000 lb. Max. dia: 10 ft. Length: 18.4 ft.	Second part of a 3-part NASA manned space flight program. A total of 7 Gemini flights were carried out in 1965 and 1966.
3-Man Spacecraft	Apollo Command Module Height: 10'7" Diameter: 12'10" Weight (incl. crew): 12,200 lb.	Third part of NASA manned flight program. First manned flight into Earth orbit October 11-22, 1968. The Command Module can be used for Earth orbital operations, but it is designed primarily for lunar missions (see Table 6).
3-to-6-Man Spacecraft	Orbital Workshop	Fourth part of NASA manned space flight program. The space installation consists of an empty S-IVB stage, equipped and furnished for human residence. Program objective is (1) to use the orbital workshop as space test facility for solving space medical, space technological, and space operational problems associated with longer stay times (upwards of 30 days) in space and on the lunar surface; (2) to be used as laboratory for developing space applications serving the nation and mankind in terms of natural resources identification and monitoring (oceanic, agricultural, forestry, water resources, air pollution, etc.); (3) to establish first orbital workshop for science (astronomy, biology); planned for 1971.
2- or 3-Man Spacecraft	Manned Lunar Orbiting Laboratory	In the planning stage for NASA's Apollo Lunar Exploration (ALEM) Program. This project involves a lunar mission similar to the original Apollo Mission, except that a landing may or may not be involved. The manned spacecraft stays in a circumlunar orbit at about 60 n.mi. altitude for about 14 days and subsequently returns to Earth, reentering the atmosphere as in the Apollo mission.
Space Stations		Large functional space installations, manned or intermittently man-attended and established in orbits about Earth or about other celestial bodies. Populations may range from some 10 to many more persons in completely self-sufficient orbital bases. Space stations are likely to come into existence in the seventies and later.

TABLE 6 INTERORBITAL SPACE VEHICLES

Interorbital Space Vehicle	Designation	Mission
Unmanned Interplanetary Spacecraft (BUS)	Mariner	Venus flyby: 1962 (Mariner II, 447 lb, ELV: Atlas Agena) Mars flyby: 1964 (Mariner IV, 557 lb, ELV: Atlas Agena) Venus flyby: 1967 (Mariner V, 540 lb, ELV: Atlas Agena) Mars flyby: 1969 (Mariner VI & VII, 1100 lb, ELV: Atlas-Centaur) Future Missions: Mars orbiter: 1971; ELV: Atlas-Centaur Venus-Mercury flyby: 1973; ELV: Atlas-Centaur Venus Orbiter: 1973 or 1975
	Modified Pioneer	Planned Missions: Jupiter flyby: 1972, 1973; ELV: Atlas-Centaur or Titan IIIC
	Viking Spacecraft	Planned Missions: Orbiting Mars and delivering a Mars Lander: 1973, 1975; ELV: Titan IIID-Centaur
	Outer Solar System Probe	Planned Missions: Prototype test in Jupiter flyby missions: 1974 Flyby mission to Jupiter-Saturn-Pluto: 1977 Flyby mission to Jupiter-Uranus-Neptune: 1979 ELV: Titan IIID-Centaur
	Advanced Mariners	Comet D'Arrest flyby: 1976 Asteroid Belt missions: 1974-78 period (Asteroid probe probably equipped with electric propulsion.) ELV: Atlas-Centaur or Titan IIID-Centaur
Manned Cislunar Interorbital Space Vehicle	Apollo Command Module Wt.: Initial (incl. crew): 12,200 lb. Splashdown: 11,700 lb. Service Module Wt.: 52,800 lb. Ht.: 22 ft. 7 in. Diameter: 12 ft. 10 in.	The first generation manned Earth-Moon Transportation system is the Apollo Spacecraft which consists of: Saturn S-IVB stage, boosting spacecraft out of Earth orbit and into a transfer orbit to the Moon Service Module whose propulsion system will inject spacecraft into a circumlunar orbit and later launch it out of this orbit back to Earth Command Module carrying the crew and serving as docking partner of the lunar module First manned flight to moon: Dec. 12-27, 1968 (Apollo 8) First manned landing on moon: July 16-24, 1969 (Apollo 11)
	Advanced Cislunar Shuttle	A not-yet-existing cislunar interorbital space vehicle, commuting routinely between Earth orbit and circumlunar orbit serving one or several lunar bases.
Manned Heliocentric Interorbital Space Vehicle		A not-yet-existing interplanetary vehicle carrying astronauts to various planets of the solar system and back. This vehicle will be powered, at least in part, by nuclear propulsion.

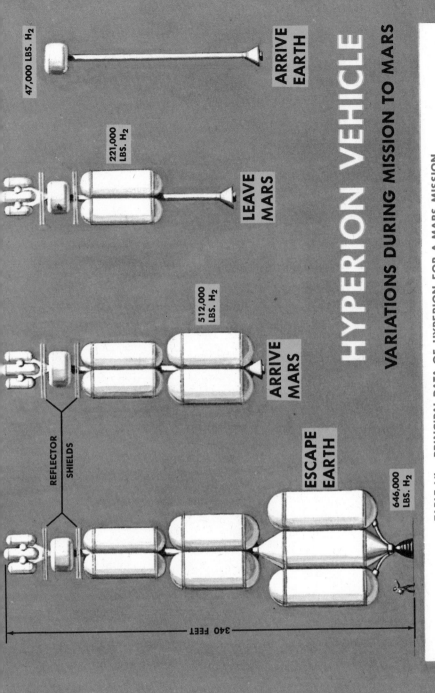

HYPERION VEHICLE

ARRIVE EARTH — 47,000 LBS. H_2

LEAVE MARS — 221,000 LBS. H_2

ARRIVE MARS — 512,000 LBS. H_2

ESCAPE EARTH — 646,000 LBS. H_2

REFLECTOR
SHIELDS

340 FEET

VARIATIONS DURING MISSION TO MARS

TABLE VI — PRINCIPAL DATA OF HYPERION FOR A MARS MISSION
Earth—Mars—Earth (347 day round trip; 4 persons)[1]

PHASE	LEAVING EARTH	ARRIVING MARS	LEAVING MARS	ARRIVING EARTH
Orbital altitude (n. mi.)	300	1,000	1,000	300
Payload weight (lb.)	58,200	53,700	51,200	20,000
H_2 weight consumed (lb.)	646,000	512,000	221,000	47,000
Initial weight (lb.)	1,590,000	912,000	355,000	85,000
Final weight (lb.)	943,500	400,500	134,500	38,000
Thrust (lb.)	650,000	10,000	10,000	10,000

1) The number of persons in one ship—It is assumed that a fleet of three to four ships will participate in the voyage.

PAYLOAD LH_2

CHEMICAL STAGE LH_2

NUCLEAR STAGE LH_2

CHEMICAL STAGE LO_2

280 FEET

HELIOS

WITH OXYGEN-HYDROGEN LIFT-OFF STAGE

Mariner instruments will penetrate the atmosphere of Mars to investigate the possibility of life

Ranger is an instrumented spacecraft designed for lunar landing

TABLE 7   DESCENT AND LANDING VEHICLES

Descent and Landing Vehicle	Designation	Mission
Manned Earth Reentry Vehicle	Mercury Gemini	In addition to their function as orbital laboratories (manned orbiting spacecraft) Mercury and Gemini also were developed to reenter the Earth's atmosphere at 17,500 mph and carry out water landing on parachute.
	Apollo Command Module	In addition to being the command module ("cockpit") of the Apollo Spacecraft, the Command Module is also designed to return into the Earth's atmosphere at 25,000 mph and land on water. Thus, the Command Module can also serve readily as a 3-man reentry vehicle from Earth orbit, if desired.
Manned Lunar Landing Vehicle	Apollo Lunar Module (LM) Propellants: Nitrogen Tetroxide (N_2O_4), 50/50 mixture of hydrazine and unsymmetrical dimethyl hydrazine (UDMH)	First generation 2-man lunar lander, used in manned Apollo Moon landings beginning 1969. Additional follow-on applications may include use of the LM as unmanned lander to deliver supplies or serve as lunar shelter for extended stay times (2 to 3 weeks) on the lunar surface. The LM consists of a descent propulsion subsystem and an ascent propulsion subsystem which carries the crew compartment. Gross weight is about 32,500 lb. (Earth). Initial weight of the re-ascending LM is approximately 18,000 lb. (Earth) or 3,000 lb. (Moon). The descent engine has a maximum thrust of 10,000 lb. and can be throttled to 1,050 lb. The ascent engine thrust is constant and equal to 3,500 lb. The descent stage serves as launch platform for the ascent stage.
Lunar Lander	Surveyor Launch Weight about 2300 lb. Landing Weight about 625 lb. (Earth). Solid propellant motor for breaking descent speed to lunar surface.	Unmanned soft-landing lunar probe. Program objectives included development of lunar landing operation and provision of scientific and engineering data in support of manned lunar landings. The program comprised 7 Surveyors, launched in 1966 to 1968. Surveyor I landed in the Ocean of Storms on June 2, 1966 and transmitted 11,150 pictures to Earth. Surveyor III, the first spacecraft to carry a claw-like digging device to test the cohesiveness of the lunar soil and to probe beneath the lunar surface, landed in the eastern portion of the Ocean of Storms on April 19, 1967. Surveyor V, the first to carry an instrument for the chemical analysis of the lunar soil, landed on September 10, 1967 in the Sea of Tranquility near the lunar equator. The lunar soil tested by Surveyor V is composed of basaltic rock similar to a type of basalt found in various places on Earth. Surveyor VI landed successfully on November 9, 1967. Surveyor VII, launched in January 1968, was the first Surveyor to land in mountainous terrain near the bright crater Tycho.
Mars Lander	Viking Lander	Unmanned soft-landing probe to be released from Viking Bus/Orbiter Spacecraft after establishment of an initial elliptic orbit about the planet. Lander is expected to stay operational for 10 days or less. Primary experiments will concern search for life (or organic substances) and investigation of Martian soil and atmosphere. Lander will transmit pictures and data to orbiter for relay to Earth. Each Viking orbiter/lander combination is lifted into parking orbit by a Titan IIID launch vehicle and injected into its trans-Mars flight path by a Centaur.

Spallanzani, Lazzaro (spahl-lahn-TZA-nee) (1729-1799) Spallanzani, an Italian Jesuit priest and biologist, discovered that *spermatazoa* are necessary for FERTILIZATION in animals. He also was the first scientist to use *artificial insemination* successfully. In addition, he proved beyond doubt that microorganisms could not develop in vegetables that had been boiled and properly kept in closed containers. These experiments were similar to those performed later by LOUIS PASTEUR.

Spallanzani was born at Reggio, Italy, on January 12, 1729. He was educated at the Jesuit College in Reggio di Modena. From there he went to the University of Bologna to study law, but instead became interested in science. After becoming a Jesuit priest, he accepted in 1756 a professorship at Reggio and later at Pavia.

Spallanzani's prolific research and experimentation in *physiology* included studies of REGENERATION, blood circulation, *respiration, gastric digestion,* and the senses of bats.   D. H. J.

SEE ALSO: SPONTANEOUS GENERATION

Spanish moss Spanish moss is not really a moss. It is a flowering plant that grows on the branches and upper parts of trees. It has tiny, yellow spike flowers that bloom on long, trailing, thread-like stems, which may grow to 20 feet in length. Because they grow so close together, the drooping stems of the Spanish moss give oak and cy-press trees a sad or ghostly appearance. When seen from a distance, these trees often seem surrounded by a thick fog.

Spanish moss is related to the pineapple. It is an *epiphyte,* a plant that lives on other plants. Its roots are not embedded in the soil. An epiphyte is not a parasite because it manufactures its own food. Spanish moss grows in tropical America.   M. R. L.

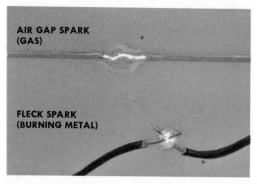

AIR GAP SPARK (GAS)

FLECK SPARK (BURNING METAL)

Spark An electric spark is a flash of light seen when an electrical charge excites the air or gas through which it passes. Current can make wires hot at points of contact and cause flecks of hot metal to flash.

SEE: STATIC ELECTRICITY

Sparrow These birds belong to the largest of the bird families, the finch family. All sparrows have the cone-shaped bill of a seedeater. Many seed-eaters are not migratory, since seeds are often available in the winter when other types of food are not. Most sparrows are medium-sized and have brownish feathers.

The species of sparrows are hard to distinguish from one another because many have streaked-brown or red-brown feathers.

Spanish moss
Courtesy Society For Visual Education, Inc.

English sparrow

In some fish species, the mating pair go through courtship activities first; then the female spawns and the male distributes the milt over the eggs in the water

One of the most common of the 90 or more species is the house or English sparrow. This bird has a gray crown, bordered from the eye backward on the neck with chestnut. Wing feathers are streaked with black and chestnut and are tipped white. The belly is whitish.

Sparrows nest almost anyplace using any material they can find. Four to seven olive-speckled white eggs are laid.   J. C. K.

Sparrow hawk see Hawk, Kestrel

Spasm (SPAZZ-uhm) When a small group of muscles begin to contract or pull together suddenly, as in rapid twitching of the eye muscles, this is called a spasm. Due to injury of the nerves, the muscles become overactive.

Spawning (SPAWN-eeng) Spawning is the laying of the eggs of fish. The eggs are called *spawn* and are laid in very large masses. After the eggs are fertilized by the male fish, they hatch. There are many ways that fish spawn.

Many fish leave their eggs unprotected after they spawn. The cod and flounder lay millions of eggs. The kinds that stay to guard their eggs after spawning lay fewer eggs. In some species, the eggs are fertilized when the male sprays sperm and liquid, called *milt,* over them; comparatively few such externally-fertilized eggs receive sperm cells and become fertile. In other species, the eggs are fertilized by the male inside the female's body opening (*cloaca*) before laying.

Some fish, such as the SUNFISH and *trout,* deposit their eggs in a depression that they make in a stream bottom. The male guards the eggs or covers them with sand for protection. Some males build a nest of *algae* and guard the eggs until they hatch. Female sea horses lay their eggs in a pouch in the male's tail, where they are carried until hatching. The female saltwater *catfish* carries its eggs in its mouth for protection.

Fresh water fish usually spawn in the water where they live. Other fish migrate hundreds and even thousands of miles to reach their spawning region. This MIGRATION of schools of fish is called a *run.* Fish that go up the river to spawn are called *anadromous.* Fish that go down the river, out to sea, are *catadromous.*

Some fish do not spawn. Their eggs hatch inside them and their young are born alive. They are *ovoviviparous.* Most sharks have young this way. Fish that spawn, laying eggs which hatch outside their bodies, are called *oviparous.*   P. G. B.

SEE ALSO: PISCES, REPRODUCTIVE SYSTEMS

Spearmint

Spearmint (SPEER-mint) Spearmint is a plant of the MINT family. The stems are long and square. The flowers grow in clusters on a stalk. The leaves look somewhat like those of peppermint but longer. They are used green or dried. They add flavor to gum and candy, medicine and beverages, such as tea.

Spearmint is an aromatic perennial that grows well in a damp environment. It is cultivated all over the world and around Lake Michigan in the United States. It is native to Asia and Europe. The essential oil stored in the cells is the main reason man grows this herb. Botanically, it is *Mentha spicata*. H. J. C.

Specialization (SPESH-uhl-uh-ZA-shun) Specialization is the dividing up of the activities of METABOLISM so that particular tissues or organs do particular jobs and are especially adapted to do these jobs. It is typical of the higher animals.

SEE: CELL, EVOLUTION

Species see Animals, classification of; Plants, classification of

Specific gravity Specific gravity is a measurement used to compare the densities of different objects. It is defined as the weight of a given substance divided by the weight of an equal volume of water. For example, a certain volume of iron weighs about eight times as much as an equal volume of water. Therefore, its specific gravity is found as follows:

$$\text{Sp. gr.} = \frac{493 \text{ lbs./cu. ft.}}{62.4 \text{ lbs./cu. ft.}} = 7.9$$

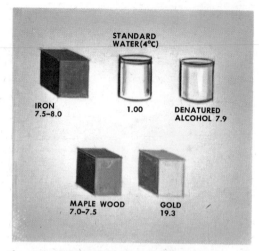

The specific gravities of substances are the weights of equal-sized amounts compared with the same amount of water taken as a standard

Water is the standard used to compare materials. Because specific gravity is a ratio, there are no units involved. In other words, the specific gravity of iron is 7.9.

The specific gravity of any object may be found by *Archimede's principle*. If an object is heavier than water, its weight in air is found. Then it is placed in water. This will make it lighter because of buoyancy. Archimede's principle states that an object placed in a fluid will be buoyed or pushed up with a force equal to the weight of water displaced. Therefore, the difference of the weight of an object in air as compared with its weight in water is equal to the weight of an equal volume of water.

Problem: A piece of metal weighs 20 lbs. in air and 12.6 lbs. in water. What kind of metal is this? The weight of water displaced equals 7.4 lbs. (20 minus 12.6)

Solution: Sp. gr. $= \dfrac{20 \text{ lbs.}}{7.4 \text{ lbs.}} = 2.7$

A table will show that aluminum has a specific gravity of 2.7.

The specific gravity of an object lighter than water may be found; but a sinker is necessary to immerse the object fully. If allowance is made for the weight of the sinker in air and water, the difference of

---

✳ **THINGS TO DO**

DO MATERIALS DIFFER IN THEIR SPECIFIC GRAVITY?

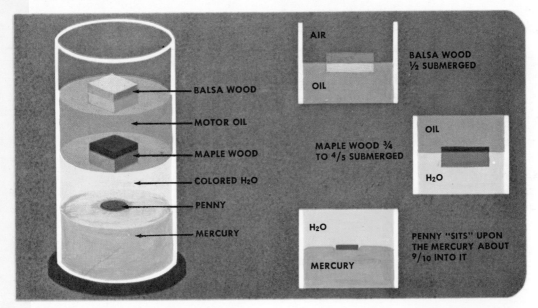

1   Pour an inch of mercury into a test tube or slender glass jar. Now put in an inch of water and of oil.

2   Cap the top and shake the solution vigorously. Set it down to settle. What happens? Which is heavier?

3   Now perform an additional test. Drop into the bottle a silver dime, a block of elm, maple, or similar wood, and a cube of balsa.

4   Observe how far down each material finally goes before it settles. Which one stays at which level?

---

the total weight and the weight of the sinker will be the weight of the object. Then calculations may be made as in the previous problem.

The specific gravity of a liquid can easily be found by using a special bottle called a *pycnometer*. By using a volume of water equal to that of the unknown and finding their weights, the specific gravity may be calculated.   E. Y. K.

SEE ALSO: ARCHIMEDES, BUOYANCY, DENSITY

Specific heat When any material is heated, it becomes warmer. Some materials require more HEAT than others to raise their temperature by a given amount; for instance, it is easier to heat metal than water. The amount of heat needed to heat one gram of a material one degree Centigrade is called its *specific heat*.

A CALORIE of heat has been defined as the amount of heat needed to raise one gram of water one degree Centigrade. Thus, the specific heat of water is one calorie per gram per degree Centigrade. Physicists find it useful to compare the heat capacity of other materials with that of water. Therefore, tables of specific heat indicate the amount of heat absorbed by a substance when one gram of it is heated through one degree Centigrade.   H. W. M.

Specimen see Microscope

	Specific Heat Calories per gram
Aluminum	0.214
Copper	0.092
Gold	0.031
Iron	0.118
Lead	0.030
Mercury	0.033
Silver	0.055

THESE ARE THE SPECIFIC HEATS OF SOME METALS AT ABOUT ROOM TEMPERATURE.

Argonne National Laboratory Photograph

A giant mass spectrometer as is used in nuclear science research

Spectrograph (SPEK-truh-graff) A spectrograph is an instrument that separates a mixture of different wavelengths of radiant energy into its parts and records the amount and position of each. It is really a SPECTROMETER that can record, usually by photography, the parts of the mixture.

An *optical* spectrograph separates white light, a mixture of colors, into the individual colors that make it up. The colors are made to fall on a photographic plate.

The amount of darkening of the plate at one particular place gives information about the amount of light from a particular color that was in the original white light. The position on the plate shows the wavelength of that particular color relative to the wavelengths of other colors.

Spectrographs can analyze and record not only visible light but also ultraviolet light, a light that has wavelengths of less than 3,600 angstroms (1 angstrom equals 10^{-8} centimeters) and infrared light, which has wavelengths greater than 7,600 angstroms. By analyzing the light emitted from atoms and molecules when they are heated or excited in some way, the spectrograph can give information about the energies of the vibration and rotation of the atoms or molecules.

F. R. W.

Spectrometer (spek-TRAH-muh-ter) A spectrometer is an instrument which separates a mixture of different wavelengths of radiation. Optical spectrometers are of two general types: the PRISM and the interference spectrometer. The first device uses a prism to separate visible light into the various wavelengths that make it up. The interference spectrometer uses a *diffraction grating* (a piece of glass with thousands of lines drawn parallel to each other for each inch of length).

If the composition of the source of light is unknown, its colored lines are like "fingerprints" that can be compared to those of known chemicals and elements. The light from stars and the reflected sunlight from planets are analyzed by astronomers to give information about the physical composition of the star or planet. Even very slight traces of elements can be detected and identified. The findings of astronomers using spectral analysis of the radiation from the SUN and stars reveal that the elements throughout the universe are distributed differently than they are on Earth.

M. B. C.

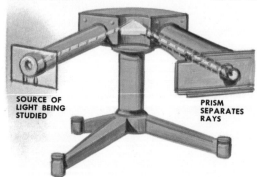

SOURCE OF LIGHT BEING STUDIED

PRISM SEPARATES RAYS

Spectrometers aid scientists in determining the composition of materials

Spectroscope (SPEK-truh-skohp) The spectroscope is an instrument used for observations of various kinds of spectra. It is not used for measurements of wavelengths and angles.

In spectroscopy, substances that radiate light in a pattern of colored lines are studied. Glowing bright lines are evidence that the light has reached the instrument directly from the source. Substances absorb light in a particular pattern. In the case of dark lines in a spectrum, radiation has passed through lower energy-level matter that has soaked up the energy of the type it would otherwise give off. The brightness (or darkness) of the lines enables scientists to calculate the weight of the amount present.

A slit of light from neon signs, mercury vapor lamps, and ordinary fluorescent lights may be viewed through a piece of plastic diffraction grating to see the bright lines characteristic of each.

A mass spectrometer separates equally charged particles in a gas according to the mass of each particle. The substance to be analyzed first is ionized. The IONS are then injected into a magnetic field. This magnetic field continuously deflects the ions around a circular path. The path will depend on the ratio of the charge of the ion to its MOMENTUM (MASS times VELOCITY). The greater the mass, the smaller the curvature of the path. Therefore, ions having the same charge and velocity but different masses will strike different places along a photographic plate.

F. R. W.

SEE ALSO: COLOR, SPECTROGRAPH, SPECTRUM, STAR

Spectrum When white light is passed through a prism, the band of colors which can be seen is called a *spectrum*. White light is a mixture of violet, blue, green, yellow, orange, and red light. Each of these colors has a different wave length. When the light is passed through a prism, it is *refracted* (bent). Light with the shorter wave lengths is bent the most. Violet light, therefore, is bent farthest as the light travels through the prism. The long red light waves are bent the least.

Light is only one type of electromagnetic radiation. Just below the visible spectrum are infrared (heat) waves. Just above the visible spectrum are ultraviolet waves. Below the infrared region is the region of radio waves. X rays and gamma rays are in the region above the ultraviolet. The entire spectrum of rays is called the *electromagnetic spectrum*.

The visible spectrum is only a very small part of the ELECTROMAGNETIC SPECTRUM but it is the only part of the spectrum that the human eye can detect. Photographic film can detect ultraviolet, infrared, and X-ray radiation.

The wave length of light is measured in *angstrom* units, named after a Swedish physicist. One angstrom is equal to 10^{-8} cm. The human eye is sensitive only to radiation in the range of 3600 (violet) to 7600 (red) angstroms.

If a spectrum obtained by passing white light through a prism is then passed through another prism, white light will again be produced. If a convex lens is used, it will also produce white light at its focus.

In the formation of a RAINBOW, the individual raindrops refract, scatter, and reflect sunlight. At certain times two rainbows may be seen. The inner bow is the brighter and is called the *primary rainbow*. Red light appears on the outside and violet on the inside. The colors are reversed in the fainter (*secondary*) rainbow.

A beam of light passing through, or reflecting from, various types of diffraction gratings will produce a spectrum. Such a grating when used in viewing glowing gases separates the light into its characteristic colors. Instead of a rainbow of color, only a few bright lines of color will be seen. Each element produces lines at characteristic positions and the positions can be used as "fingerprints" in identifying the element.

ISAAC NEWTON experimented with mixing spectral colors. A mixture of light from slits at orange and green produces yellow. The *classic color triangle* was developed for use in predicting the colors that would be seen when spectral rays were focused on a screen.

Å = ANGSTROM UNITS

| 3600–4300 Å | 4300–4550 Å | 4550–4920 Å | 4920–5500 Å | 5500–5880 Å | 5800–6470 Å | 6470–7600 Å |

A dark-line spectrum, one from which certain colors are missing, generally indicates that white LIGHT has passed through a substance that has absorbed certain wave lengths. Such lines in the sun's spectrum were discovered by Fraunhofer and are named after him. The lines give evidence of elements existing in the sun's atmosphere which absorb certain wavelengths of the sun's radiation. The spectra of the stars are studied to determine their temperatures and compositions.   F. R. W.

SEE ALSO: COLOR, LIGHT

Speech see Voice

Speed
As an object moves, a most important question one may ask is, "How fast is it moving?" Speed refers to the rate of MOTION—the distance traveled in a fixed time. If a car travels 1000 feet in 10 seconds, the average speed is 100 feet per second.

Speed is easily computed by the relationship $s = d/t$, where s is the average speed, d the distance covered and t the given time. Speed is normally expressed in feet per second, miles per hour, or in whatever units d and t are represented.   I. K. F.

SEE ALSO: ACCELERATION, VELOCITY

Speed of sound
Sound travels about 765 miles per hour through air at sea level and at 32° F. Greater speeds through liquids and solids are due to higher densities.

Sperm
(SPUHRM) Sperms are tiny cells that move by whiplike processes called FLAGELLA. They are the GAMETES made by male parts of plants or animals. Union with an egg is called FERTILIZATION and results in a ZYGOTE, which eventually develops into an adult.

In lower plants, one cell divides many times to form sperms. In plants like a MOSS, sperms are formed in a sex organ, the antheridium. In a plant like a rose, sperm are part of the *pollen* grains. They are formed in sacs called *anthers* at the tips of the floral STAMEN

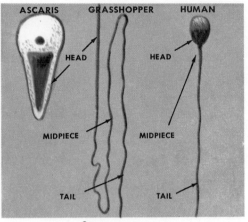

Some sperm types

In animals, sperms are formed in the male sex organ, or TESTIS, and are the end result of a process called MEIOSIS.

A typical sperm consists of a *head,* a *neck* or *midpiece,* and a *tail* or flagellum. The head is mostly *chromatin* carrying the GENES for male hereditary characteristics. The midpiece carries *centrioles* to control movement and *mitochondria* to furnish needed energy.
                    J. C. K.

Sperm whale see Whale

Spermaceti see Whale

Spermatophyte (spuhr-MAA-toh-fite)
Spermatophyte is the name of a plant belonging to the highest of the four *phyla* into which the plant kingdom was divided under the old system of plant classification. It includes the classes *gymnosperm* and *angiosperm* — the seed-producing plants. Both classes are now in subdivision *Pteropsida,* division *Tracheophyta.*

SEE: PLANTS, CLASSIFICATION OF

Spermatozoa see Sperm

Sperry, Elmer Ambrose (1860-1930)
Elmer Ambrose Sperry, American inventor and manufacturer, was born in Cortland, New York. Though his many inventions include the ARC lamp first used in street lighting and later in giant searchlights, he is best known for his use of the gyroscope.

His gyrocompass, first installed on the battleship *Delaware* in 1911, was not affected by iron and steel of the ship, or by magnetic forces of the earth. He also invented gyropilots for steering ships, and installed gyroscopes in ships and aircraft to steady rolling motions. Naval gunnery and air navigation are based upon his inventions with the gyroscope. Sperry also founded two societies for electrical and electrochemical engineers. D. H. J.

SEE ALSO: GYROSCOPE

Sphagnum see Moss, Peat

Sphere see Geometry

Spherical symmetry see Animals, classification of

Sphincter (SFINGK-tuhr) A sphincter is a ring of muscle fibers which surround a body opening, a hollow organ, or a duct opening. The fibers contract to make the opening smaller or close it altogether. These muscles are in the pylorus and the anus.

SEE: DIGESTIVE SYSTEM

Spice Spice is a sharp-tasting, pungent-smelling plant or plant product. Spices are taken from the part of the plant that is richest in flavor. It may be a piece of sweet-smelling bark, as in the case of CINNAMON. Ginger comes from the root, cloves from the flower bud, PEPPER from the fruit, nutmeg from the kernel, and mace from the kernel wrapper. Most spices are grown in tropical countries. *Caraway, coriander, dill,* and *ginger* have been successfully cultivated in temperate climates. Some gardeners have their own backyard spice and herb gardens.

Spices have little food value. They are used to stimulate the organs of digestion and increase the appetite. Many spices have other commercial uses besides flavorings for food and drink. They are used in medicines, perfumes, incense, and soap. Pepper is a stimulating condiment. Cloves and cinnamon are used for aromatics. Some

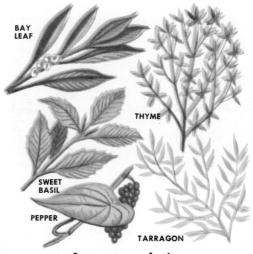

BAY LEAF

THYME

SWEET BASIL

PEPPER

TARRAGON

Some sources of spices

spices are used as powders and others as *tinctures* made from oils of the various spice plants.

Spices have played an important role in world history. Not only did the search for spices lead to the discovery of America and the sea route to the Far East, but for centuries the desire for spices has caused wars, determined the rise and fall of states, and even twice remade the world's religious history. J. K. K.

Spicule (SPIK-yule) A spicule is a hard, needle-like, limy or siliceous structure which forms within the tissues of certain *invertebrates* such as *sponges.* The spicules act as a SKELETON to stiffen and support. They may look like rods or may have complex and beautiful forms, like snow crystals.

SEE: PORIFERA

Sponge spicules

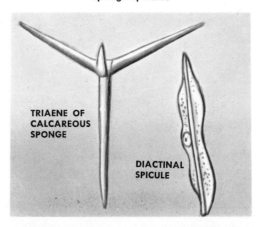

TRIAENE OF CALCAREOUS SPONGE

DIACTINAL SPICULE

Helen J. Challand
Spider plant

Courtesy Society For Visual Education, Inc.
Garden spider

Spider plant The spider plant, also called the *bee plant, skunkweed,* or *electric light* plant, is a tall, bushy herb about three to eight feet tall. It grows wild in the western plains of the United States and also is cultivated in gardens.

The spider plant is an annual which grows from spring to early fall. Its pink, yellow, and lilac flowers grow in large, loose clusters. It has smooth stems and long, flat seed pods. When crushed, the leaves and stems have a strong, unpleasant odor. There are seven species of spider plants; they belong to the Caper family. The scientific name of the most common spider plant is *Cleome spinosa.*   D. J. A.

Spiders (SPY-duhrs) Spiders are insectlike animals. They have eight legs, but no feelers or wings. Their bodies are divided into two parts, and they have waists but no necks. Most are near-sighted even with eight simple eyes. Spiders look like little adults when they hatch from eggs. They eat insects and other spiders, even their sisters and brothers. Young spiders, without being shown how, will spin webs to catch their food.

Most spiders are *terrestrial* (land-living). The fresh-water spider lives in a dome-shaped web under water. This serves to hold air. The spider ascends, traps air, descends, and deposits it in its web. Water spiders run along the surface of ponds searching for food.

Garden spiders are "fliers." Climbing up

Grass spider (left), black widow spider (right)

on tall grass, they will spin a balloon-like structure. Strong wind will carry the spider thousands of feet into the air.

White crabspiders change their outfits to match the surroundings. If they spend most of their time on yellow flowers, they will molt and appear with a yellow exterior. *Grass spiders* spin funnel webs, then casually sit at the bottom waiting for some unsuspecting insect to tumble down it.

The *black widow* is the only poisonous spider in the United States. The female is coal black with a red hour-glass spot on the underside of the abdomen. The males are smaller and harmless.

The *wolf spider* stalks its prey by running after it. It lives in burrows in the ground and carries the egg sac with it when it leaves.

The large hairy *tarantula* may exceed a half foot in length. The bite of this spider is extremely painful but not fatal. It does not spin a web. It hides in the daytime and stalks its prey at night, sometimes capturing birds or fish for food.

Spiders breathe through air tubes or book lungs. Their circulatory system is open and the excretory tubules empty into the intestine. The two sharp fangs (*cheliceras*) poison their prey so the pharynx and

Spiderwort see Wild flowers

✳ THINGS TO DO

PRESERVING SPIDER WEBS

Materials: black or dark construction paper, a can of clear plastic adhesive spray.

1 Locate a spider's web. They are found in a variety of places; corners of buildings, across strands of tall grass and shrubs, and between rows of corn in a field. They may be in corners of dark storage rooms.

2 Carefully place the paper on one side of the web until it touches. Gently spray the plastic into the web. When it dries the web will be permanently cemented to the paper.

3 Collect as many as you can find that are constructed in different patterns and shapes. What kind of spider spun each one?

stomach can suck the juices. The digestive gland is large and will store enough food to last the spider for weeks. Spiders have a pair of sensory appendages (*pedipalps*) which enable them to pick up any movement near them.

Spinnerets secrete a liquid from silk glands. When this hits the air, it hardens. Webs are made in interesting shapes— funnel, orb, hammock, bowl, or dome-shaped. Some have spun a web a yard wide in one hour. Webs are used by spiders to travel, line nests, wrap eggs, and catch insects. H. J. C.

SEE ALSO: ARACHNIDA

Spiderwort see Wild flowers

Spinach (SPIN-utch) Spinach is a plant that must be planted each year because it is an ANNUAL. It is called a cool-season plant because it is harvested in fall or in spring. The large arrow-shaped leaves are used either raw or cooked.

Growing leaves form a thick cir-

cular cluster close to the ground. Flowers are borne on a tall branching floral stem growing from the center of a leaf cluster.

Spinach is a *dioecious* plant since some plants have male or *staminate* flowers and others have female or *pistillate* flowers. In the flower of the male plant there are four to five stamens in the center of a five-part (lobed) *calyx*. A female flower contains a single ovary with four to five styles, each topped by a stigma. The calyx surrounding the ovary becomes hardened around the fruit developing from the ovary. The fruit is called an *achene*. Spinach belongs to the goosefoot family. J. C. K.

Spinach

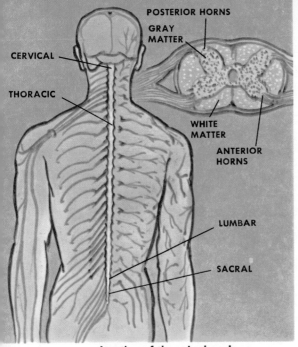

POSTERIOR HORNS
GRAY MATTER
CERVICAL
THORACIC
WHITE MATTER
ANTERIOR HORNS
LUMBAR
SACRAL

Location of the spinal cord

Spinal cord (SPINE-uhl) In adult man the spinal cord is a tube about 17 inches long. The cord connects with the BRAIN at the base of the skull. It extends through the center of the first 22 bony *vertebrae* and is protected by them.

The thick walls of the cord are made of thousands of nerve fibers. Most of the nerves coming in from the outer parts of the body send their messages (impulses) to the brain or to other parts of the cord over the fibers of the cord. These fibers also conduct impulses from the brain and the cord. The center of the cord, the *neural canal,* is very small. The cord is enlarged in two places: the *cervical* enlargement is located where all the nerves supplying the arms enter the cord. The *lumbar* enlargement is farther down in the lower back region where the nerves from the legs enter. Below the lumbar enlargement the cord tapers off into a cone-shaped end.

Each nerve entering the cord branches into two roots, a *dorsal* one with a *ganglion* (group of nerve cell bodies) and a *ventral* one. Impulses going *to* the brain or cord (*afferent*) travel over the dorsal root while

Spinal cord

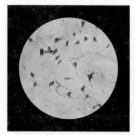

Cross section of spinal cord. The large blue irregular shapes are nerve cells and the red streaks blood vessels
Photo-micrographs by
National Teaching Aids, Inc.

those coming *from* the brain or cord (*efferent*) use the ventral root.

The cord is well protected from the hard, bony surfaces of the vertebrae. On the outside is a layer of fatty tissue containing small blood vessels. Underneath this layer are three connective tissue membranes, or *meninges.* The outer one is called the *dura mater,* the middle one is the *arachnoid,* and the innermost one is known as the *pia mater.* Between the middle and inner membrane is a cavity (*arachnoid space*) filled with *spinal fluid.* This fluid cushion is an additional protection.

Delicate nerve fibers within the cord are supported by special kinds of nonnervous cells, the *neuroglia* cells. These cells have processes which form a supporting framework between the *axons* and *dendrites* of the nerve cells.

A slice through any part of the spinal cord shows two different kinds of material. The center of the slice, or section, is made up of gray matter arranged somewhat like the letter "H." The two upper prongs of the "H" represent the dorsal horns of the gray matter. Nerve fibers coming in through the dorsal roots reach the dorsal horns. The two lower prongs of the "H" correspond to the ventral horns. Nerve fibers from the ventral horns leave by way of the ventral roots. The connecting bar across the "H" represents a connecting bar of gray matter in the center of which is the neural canal. Gray matter is composed of nerve cell bodies, dendrites, blood vessels, and *myelinated* and *unmyelinated* fibers (with and without a special covering). Nerve cells take care of sensory impulses, muscle activity, and the functioning of some of the blood vessels and internal organs.

Surrounding the H-shaped gray matter is the white matter of the cord. Long myelinated fibers arranged in bundles make up the white substance. Furrows extending in from the outer surface of the cord

1648

divide the white matter into long columns of nerve fibers called *funiculi*. The fibers in the white matter connect dorsal and ventral root fibers with different parts of the brain and spinal cord.   J. C. K.

SEE ALSO: NERVE CELL, NERVOUS SYSTEM

Spiny anteater (SPY-nee) The spiny anteater is found in Australia, Tasmania, and New Guinea. It resembles a porcupine. Although it is a mammal, it lays eggs.

The spiny anteater, or *Echidna,* is about 12 to 20 inches long. For protection, it has thick, coarse fur and many spines, somewhat like porcupines and hedgehogs. This odd animal has clawed feet for scratching and tearing apart insect nests. It also has a flattened, beak-like nose from which a long, sticky tongue darts forth, catches up ants, and brings them into the mouth to be swallowed.

The female echidna lays two white, leathery eggs, the size of sparrow eggs. These are placed in a pouch on the underside of the body. The babies live there a few weeks after hatching.

Echidnas and platypuses are the only egg-laying mammals. Their order, *Monotremata,* has the most primitive mammals and shows a relationship to reptiles.   D. J. I.

SEE ALSO: DUCKBILL, MAMMALIA

Spiny anteater

Spiracle (SPY-ruh-kuhl) Spiracles are the small openings in the body of insects through which they breathe. Spiracles may be compared to the nostrils of a human being. They are usually located along the sides of the *thorax* and *abdomen* of the insect.

Insects, unlike human beings, have no lungs. Larger kinds of insects have branch-

Section of the abdomen of a grasshopper showing spiracles, or breathing holes (A)

Photo-micrographs by National Teaching Aids, Inc.

ing tubes called *tracheal tubes* which carry oxygen to the blood stream. The tracheal tubes of some insects form large, thin-walled air sacs.

Spiracles are the surface openings of the tracheal tubes. Surrounding the spiracle is a ringlike muscle called a *sphincter*. This muscle closes the spiracle until oxygen is needed. The spiracles open more often when the insect is active, thus providing an increased supply of oxygen. The presence of carbon dioxide in the body of the insect serves as a stimulus to open the spiracles and allows the exchange of respiratory gases for oxygen.

The body walls of grasshoppers, crickets, and some other insects contract and expand, thus pumping air into and out of the tracheal tubes. In small insects, oxygen passes directly from the tubeless spiracles to the tissues by means of *diffusion*. I. H. S.

SEE ALSO: INSECTA

Spiraea (spy-REE-uh) Spiraea is a group of plants containing only shrubs. All spiraeas belong to the rose family. Many kinds flower in June and are called *bridal wreath*. A common field species is the *meadow sweet*. Graceful sprays bear clusters of small white, pink, or red flowers.

Spiraea leaves have notched edges and are attached to the branch by a short stem (petiole). Each of the flowers in a cluster has five rounded petals and one pistil surrounded by 15 to 60 stamens. The simple, "dry fruit" is a *follicle* opening on one seam.   J. C. K.

Spirilla see Bacteria

Spiraea

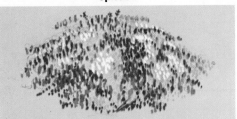

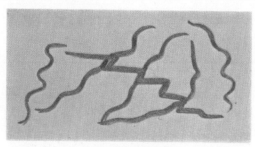

Syphilis spirochetes

Spirochetes (SPY-ruh-keets) Spirochetes make up a special group of rod-like, spirally-twisted BACTERIA. The spirochetes differ in size, some of them being very small and others much larger.

Spirochetes are long, flexible, threadlike spirals with a length about 20 times their width. Some seem flattened and appear more like spirally-curved ribbons than rods. Under ordinary conditions they move swiftly by rotation or lashing. They reproduce by transverse, *binary fission.*

Some diseases caused by species of the smaller spirochetes are relapsing fever, *syphilis,* and *yaws.* D. C. H.

SEE ALSO: BACTERIOLOGY

Spirogyra (SPY-row-jy-rah) Spirogyra is one of the simplest forms of green plants belonging to a larger group called *algae.* It may be found in ponds, streams, or other water areas since it needs water for fertilization. The individual cells live in *filaments* or long cells joined end to end. The *chloroplast* in each cell is ribbon-shaped. Each cell has a definite cell wall, *cytoplasm,* and *nucleus,* enabling it to carry on all life functions.

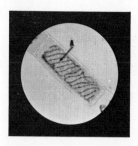

Spirogyra is a green plant complete in a single cell. (A) is the chloroplast with which it makes food

Photo-micrographs by National Teaching Aids, Inc.

Spirogyra will reproduce asexually by spores or sexually by a method called *conjugation.* The *protoplasm* in a cell rolls into a ball, breaks through the cell walls and joins the protoplasm in the adjoining cell. This mass of two cells is called a ZYGOTE. It divides several times forming *spores,* asexual reproductive bodies. When a spore escapes into the water it will grow into a new filament of spirogyra.

Spirogyra is eaten by many aquatic animals. Man uses this seaweed as the basis for several products including puddings, creams, and polishes. H. J. C.

SEE ALSO: ALGAE, THALLOPHYTES

Spleen The spleen is a gland that makes some of the white blood cells, destroys old red blood cells, and stores blood. In humans, the spleen is a rounded, reddish organ about five inches wide and three inches long. It is found behind the stomach.

The front half of the spleen is concave to fit around the curve of the stomach, and the posterior part is molded onto the edge of the left kidney. The borders have several notches. The blood vessels enter and leave at the *hilum,* which is just in front of a prominent internal ridge that divides the spleen into two parts. The spleen has a covering of *fibroelastic tissue* which contains muscle. This coating sends partitions into the spleen; these subdivide the organ into tiny compartments where the spleen pulp is found. Spleen pulp is red and has small, round masses of *tissue, blood vessels* sheathed in lymphatic tissue, red blood *corpuscles, lymphocytes* (a type of white cell), and cells with pigment or fat.

In regulating the volume of blood in the body, the spleen is able to act as a reservoir, holding one fifth of all the blood. The spleen is part of the lymphatic and circulatory systems.

In animals without backbones (*invertebrates*), the spleen is a mass of lymphatic tissue stretched all along the *alimentary canal* of the *digestive system.* The spleen is not a distinct gland in the simpler vertebrates, but in sharks it is divided into small lobes. In fish the spleen is against the stomach and even sometimes (*Protopterus, Dipnoi*) in the stomach wall. In frogs and

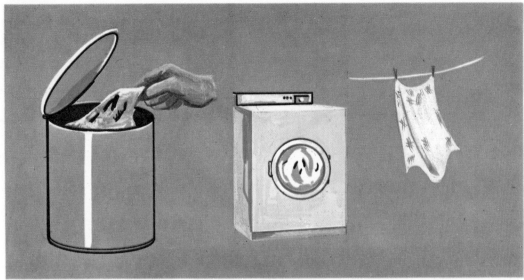

To prevent fires from spontaneous combustion, all oily rags or clothing should be either (1) put in airtight metal cans or (2) immediately washed and hung to dry

toads the spleen is a round mass close to the upper end of the *cloaca*. Vegetable-eating animals usually have smaller spleens with fewer notches than do animals that eat flesh.   E. M. S.

SEE ALSO: BLOOD, BLOOD TYPES, CIRCULATORY SYSTEM, ENDOCRINE GLANDS, LYMPHATIC SYSTEM

Sponge see Porifera

Spleen regulates blood flow
©Denoyer-Geppert Co.

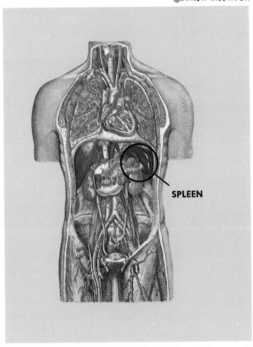

SPLEEN

Spontaneous combustion (spahn-TAY-nee-uhs) Spontaneous combustion occurs when an object burns without the help of a match or open flame. This may happen when rags and other materials soaked with oil or such combustible fluids as turpentine, gasoline, kerosene, and linseed oil are stored in an enclosed space, like a box or closet. It can even happen to piled newspapers.

Combustion is the rapid combination of oxygen with a fuel. Spontaneous combustion is a combination of oxygen with carbon and hydrogen in the oil. When reactive oils are finely coated on fabrics in an enclosed space, this combination slowly raises the temperature until the kindling point of the oil and fabric is reached. Then the material will burst into flames and may cause a serious fire.

Precautions must be taken against spontaneous combustion, especially around the home where many flammable liquids are used with rags. Rags or other materials soaked with combustible liquids should not be stored in any enclosed space, including the basement or attic. Instead, they should be put into an airtight metal can or immediately washed and hung out to dry.

E. Y. K.

SEE ALSO: COMBUSTION

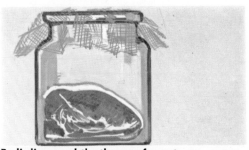

Redi disproved the theory of spontaneous generation by the simple method of covering rotting meat. Flies were not able to lay eggs in it and more flies could not develop

Spontaneous generation Another name for spontaneous generation is *abiogenesis*. Both terms refer to a theory which states some living organisms originate or start from nonliving materials. Most scientists held this theory in the eighteenth century. It was disproved in the late nineteenth century.

The belief in abiogenesis assumed that frogs came from mud, insects from dew, and flies from decaying meat. The *maggot* or larval stage of flies was not, at that time, associated with the adult FLY.

In 1668 an Italian physician, Francesco Redi, disproved this theory by exposing meat in covered and uncovered jars. Only meat in the uncovered jars had flies. His work was not taken seriously by other scientists. In 1767 another Italian, Lazaro Spallanzani, placed boiled extracts of meat in flasks sealed with heat and in open flasks. Organisms developed in the open flasks but not in the sealed ones. Again other scientists objected, claiming that heat destroyed something in the air inside of the flasks that was necessary for the generation of life. It was not until after PASTEUR's work in 1861 that the theory of abiogenesis was finally discarded.

In the twentieth century, a more sophisticated and restrictive theory of abiogenesis was proposed. According to this theory, simple compounds like methane, ammonia, and water evolved into amino acids and proteins. Proteins further evolved into self-duplicating molecules and enzyme systems. Eventually living cells, remote ancestors of plants and animals on Earth today, came into existence. Chaotic conditions, no longer present within the climate and atmosphere, brought about this EVOLUTION.   J. C. K.

Spoonbill

Spoonbill This large wading bird is related to the HERON. Its broad, flat bill has a spoonlike tip which is used to catch small water animals for food.

Sporangium see Mold

Spore formation Plants without flowers reproduce by scattering spores instead of seeds. Most one-celled spores can be seen only with a microscope. The plant forms spores in spore cases called *sporangia*. Sporangia, visible to the naked eye, are the brown *pustules* on the underside of fern leaves, mushroom caps, stemmed capsules of mosses, and cones on the end of stalks of horsetails. These spore cases release the spores which are, in turn, carried about by the wind or by insects. They come to rest on, and grow into, molds, mosses, ferns, mushrooms, rusts, or similar plants. Water molds, *algae,* and some *protozoa* release spores into water or moisture. Swimming spores are called *zoospores.*

There are sexual and asexual spores. Asexual spores are formed through simple cell division usually by pinching themselves off from tips of threadlike *hyphae* into a sporangium.

In flowering plants the pollen grain is a *microspore,* and the *megaspore* is found in the ovule. One nucleus of the microspore forms the pollen tube, while the second nucleus unites with one of the eight

All pictures Courtesy Society For Visual Education, Inc.

In mosses, the fertilized egg develops into spore case

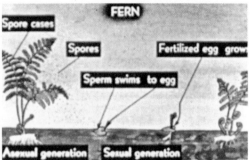

Fern spores become tiny green plants whose sperm and egg produce a fern

Dark areas on underside of fern leaf indicate spore sacs

Closeup shows tiny spore-producing organs when spores are ripe

nuclei of the megaspore. The product of this union is called a *zygote*.

Some plants produce asexual spores in one generation and sexual spores the next. This method of reproduction is called alternation of generation, with the two generations quite different in appearance.   E. M. S.

SEE ALSO: ALTERATION OF GENERATION, GAMETOPHYTE, SPOROPHYTE, ZYGOTE

Sporophyte (SPOHR-uh-fyte) Many plants go through two stages in their life history. The first occurs when a plant, or generation, produces eggs and sperms. The union of these sex cells grows into the second stage, which is called the sporophyte. At this stage, the plant produces spores, or asexual cells.

In most of the higher plants, the sporophyte is the most conspicuous plant. All of the evergreens and flowering plants are sporophytes. The *gametophyte* plant is very tiny and found within the cone, or flower, of the sporophyte. The familiar fern is a sporophyte. The spores produce a small, independent sex plant, in most cases smaller than a dime. The moss and liverwort sporophytes depend on, and grow from, the gametophyte plant.   E. M. S.

SEE ALSO: ALTERNATION OF GENERATION

Evergreens are sporophytes

Sprain A sprain is an injury to ligaments, the bands of fibrous tissue that hold bones together. A sprain occurs when a body part, especially a hand or foot, is forcibly bent in a way the joint does not normally allow. When the ligaments are torn, there is swelling and pain.

SEE: FIBROUS TISSUE, SKELETON

Spring (mechanical) A spring is an elastic body which will return to its natural shape. Springs are usually one of three types: spiral springs (as in a watch) which store energy, and coil springs (railway car) and leaf or laminated springs which cushion shock.

Spring see River, Seasons

American Forest Products Industries, Inc.
White spruce

POINSETTIA HEVEA SNOW-ON-THE-MOUNTAI
The spurge family contains trees, plants, and bushes

Spruce Spruces are trees that belong to the PINE family. They are in a different group (genus *Picea*) from either the true pines or the firs. These trees are evergreens and have needlelike leaves. They are usually tall and pyramid-shaped with spreading branches coming off the trunk in a circular fashion (whorled). Tall spruces are valuable as lumber.

Needles, borne on small projections (*sterigmata*) from the twig, are generally four-sided and white-lined. White lines are made by the openings of pores (stomata). Fir trees bear their needles in small depressions.

Spruces are *monoecious,* male and female cones occurring on the same tree. Male cones, yellow or red, persist only until pollen matures. Female cones mature in one year and hang down. Scales of the cone do not drop after the winged seeds are shed.   J. C. K.

Spurge Spurge, or *Euphorbia,* is the name for a plant family which has over 5000 members. It includes some trees, some bushes, and some small plants. The India rubber tree and the castor oil plants are members of the spurge family.

Some spurge grow in the desert and look like cactus, although they are not related. The leaves of these varieties are only small, spikey bumps and their stems are large, thick, and juicy.

Usually, members of the spurge family have brightly-colored leaves or flower bracts that are far showier than their rather small and colorless flowers. The POINSETTIA is an example of such a spurge.

Most spurge contain a milky, sometimes poisonous, juice. In certain species, this is *latex,* a source of RUBBER.

Although chiefly tropical, spurges are found all over the world.   J. M. C.

Squab see Pigeon

Squall line A large mass of advancing cold air often creates storms as it encounters warm air. The edge of the *cold front* is then described by the weatherman and indicated on his maps as a squall line. A squall is a thunderstorm which occurs in this area. In the United States, this kind of storm is called a *line squall*. With it are abrupt changes in wind direction and a quick drop in temperature. Such a storm in Argentina is called a *pompero*.

Squall zones are one of the greatest hazards to flying. A number of air accidents never completely solved are attributed to sudden encounters with these violent winds, which are capable of ripping an airplane apart. The pilot avoids squall zones because he knows that even the JET STREAM can be pushed from its path by a sudden advance of cold polar air.

By just looking at a thunder cloud, it is difficult to realize the violence of the battle going on within it as cold air grapples with warm air. These storms are localized and are accompanied by thunder and lightning, heavy rain, and sometimes hail stones driven by strong gusts of wind.   E. M. N.

SEE ALSO: AIR MASSES, WEATHER MAP

Square see Geometry

Squash The squash plant is a bush or vine belonging to the *gourd family*. The fruit is used as a vegetable. The seeds are rich in oil. The pumpkin is one type of squash.

These annual cucurbits (of genus *Cucurbita*) have large, yellow monoecious flowers which are insect pollinated. The fruit is classified as an *accessory fruit* or *false berry*. The fleshy edible part is both ripened ovary and floral tube.

Squashes are probably of American origin. They may be infected by fungi and mosaic viruses. The squash bug is also a pest. H. J. C.

Some squash fruit

Squid (SKWIDD) Long ago, sailors told stories of dragons and giant sea serpents. Most of these tales were not true; but, today, it is thought that the animals the sailors described were probably giant squid. Most squid range from several inches to two feet in length, but the giant squid can be more than 50 feet long with huge, bulging eyes. Fortunately, this monster lives only in the deepest parts of the North Atlantic. A giant squid has never been captured alive, but its remains have been washed ashore, or found in the stomachs of sperm whales.

Squids are soft-bodied animals that belong to the class *Cephalopoda,* a name which means "head-footed." The squid, like the *octopus,* has this name because its arms extend from its head. Ten sucker-bearing arms are modified from the foot common to all mollusks. Two arms, or *tentacles,* are much

Buchsbaum

Squid

longer than the others and are used to seize food. Squid feed on smaller fish; but, in turn, the squid is food for larger sea animals.

The mouth is situated at the center and base of the tentacles. It is composed of two jaws which resemble a beak. The beak bites and tears food. The *radula,* or inner tooth-like structure, further breaks up food. The egg cases are called *sea mops* because thousands of eggs are contained in bunches of long, gelatinous strings.

This mollusk's slender body is enclosed in a muscular sheath called a *mantle*. A narrow vestige of a shell is within the mantle. The shape of this tapering shell resembles a pen; and since squid eject an inky substance when excited, they have been called *pen and ink fish*. The mantle, with its two undulating finlike projections, is the chief organ for forward swimming. Water circulates through the mantle cavity and when violently ejected provides the jet-propelled backward movement. This propulsion will even lift squids out of water. J. A. D.

SEE ALSO: MOLLUSCA, OCTOPUS

Squirrel Squirrels belong to the same group as mice, beavers and other gnawing animals—the *rodents*. There are many varieties of squirrels and they are found in all countries except Australia and Madagascar. They are small furry animals with long, bushy tails. Their long front teeth grow all their lives but are kept worn to a comfortable length by gnawing and cracking nuts and seeds. Squirrels also eat toadstools and mushrooms, which

From left to right: red squirrel, gray squirrel, fox squirrel, flying squirrel

they dry and cure in the sun, and occasionally birds' eggs and baby birds.

Squirrels keep their lovely tails well groomed and use them to balance themselves as they perch precariously on tree branches and when they leap from branch to branch. Some kinds of squirrels live mostly in trees. Others spend their time on the ground. Squirrels are also grouped by color and size.

Most common in the eastern United States are the *gray squirrels*. They are often seen in parks and towns. Sometimes they become quite tame. They seem to prefer living in deciduous trees, such as hickory, oak and maple. Gray squirrels are about nine inches in body length.

Smaller than the gray squirrel is the tree-dwelling *red squirrel*. It seems to seek out evergreen trees, finding good food in the seeds of the cones. The red squirrel has rust-colored fur on its back and is striped with black. Its belly is white. Red squirrels are famous for their noisy chattering and habits of "scolding."

Squirrels are hoarders. They collect nuts and seeds and hide them in hollow trees or bury them. The seeds that are not remembered and dug up may sprout into trees. The squirrel is an asset to forests.

Squirrels build nests of twigs, leaves and bark. Their winter nests are in hollow trees. Most of them do not hibernate. In summer they build nests in the forks of branches. Squirrels mate usually around February and bear two to six offspring at a time. Newborn squirrels are not well developed. They are very small, have no fur, cannot see and depend on their mothers for several months.

Fox squirrels and *flying squirrels* are other American tree squirrels. *Ground squirrels* include woodchucks, chipmunks, marmots, and prairie dogs.   C. L. K.

SEE ALSO: RODENTIA

Stability   see Compounds, stability of

Stabilizer (airplane)   see Airplane, Gyroscope

Staining Staining means changing the color of an object without hiding its surface. When a piece of wood is stained, the color is different from the natural color, but the lines, or grain, of the wood show through. Painting the wood changes the color, but the paint also hides the surface of the wood.

Glass can also be stained. Stained glass is used to make beautiful ornamental windows. It is made by adding different metallic oxides to the molten mass before it is blown into glass.

In histology, cells are stained so they will be visible for study with a microscope. The dyes, which are absorbed by the cells, may not kill the cells, although all dyes are toxic to a degree. Different dyes stain different parts of the cell.

Because it is helpful for visibility to stain some cell types while they are alive, dyes are sometimes injected into tissue of living organisms. Cells that absorb the dyes can then be removed for study in thin pieces under a microscope.   C. L. K.

SEE ALSO: COLOR, DYES, GLASS, HISTOLOGY, TISSUE CULTURE

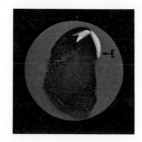

Staining helps in identifying tissue. The cotyledon (large dark mass) on this bean seed has been stained with iodine. E is the developing embryo

Photo-micrographs by National Teaching Aids, Inc.

HOW ARE FORMATIONS IN CAVES OR CAVERNS MADE?

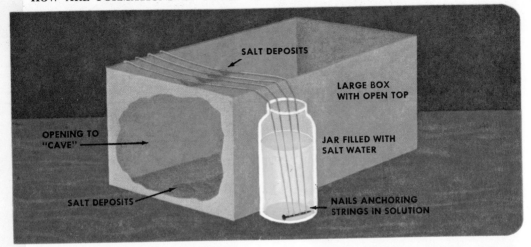

SALT DEPOSITS

LARGE BOX WITH OPEN TOP

OPENING TO "CAVE"

JAR FILLED WITH SALT WATER

SALT DEPOSITS

NAILS ANCHORING STRINGS IN SOLUTION

1   Construct a mock-up of an underground cavern with a cardboard or metal box. Follow the illustration or pattern your project after one you have seen. Place two tall jars on either side of the box. Tie four or five pieces of heavy string to two nails.

2   Make a solution of Epsom salts and water. A little vegetable dye may be added for color. Fill the jars with the solution.

3   Place a nail in each jar with the strings leading up and over the top of the open box. Water and salt will move up the cord. As the water evaporates the salt will accumulate. Leave this alone for a week.

4   Soon piles of salt build up on the floor of your homemade cave. What are they called? The formations hanging from the strings or roof are referred to as what?

Stalagmite and stalactite A stalagmite is a cone-shaped geologic formation. This is formed from calcium deposits that collect on the floor of a cave in a particular manner. A stalactite hangs from the roof.

Not all material carried by water is suspended; therefore, some materials settle. Water also carries dissolved materials or solutions that are deposited only when the water evaporates or some other chemical changes take place. Water seeping through the limestone of a cave comes out on the ceiling in droplets. Some of the dissolved carbon-dioxide gas in the water escapes into the air of the cave. Then the water can no longer keep the *calcium* compounds in solution. Each drop leaves a little deposit on the ceiling or on the floor of the cave. Over a period of time, the layers of these deposits build interesting and unusual rock formations. When the droplets do not fall to the floor but hang suspended, icicle-like stalactites are formed.

Where the water drips onto the floor of a cave, cone-shaped stalagmites are built up. When a stalactite and a stalagmite meet, a column is formed. Some water runs down the sides of a cave, and layers of stone are also formed there.   V. V. N.

Meeting stalagmites and stalactites in Mammoth Cave, Kentucky

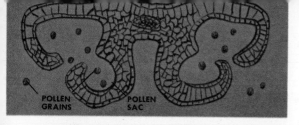

Cross section of an anther on a stamen

Stamen (STAY-mun) The stamen is the part of a flower that bears the pollen, or male cell. Each stamen is made up of a slender stalk (*filament*) topped by a sac (*anther*). Pollen sacs break open to let the pollen out. If a POLLEN grain reaches an egg in the female part of a flower, fertilization takes place.

In simple flowers, such as tulips and daisies, the stamens and *pistil* grow in the center of a cluster of petals. Some flowers have only stamens, whereas others have only pistils.   I. H. S.

Standing wave When two waves of the same frequency and kind travel through the same system, they appear to blend together. This pattern of wave blending, which seems to remain at rest, is called a standing wave. The two waves are both moving at their normal speeds in the system, usually in opposite directions.

These two waves may be any of three kinds: (1) *electromagnetic,* consisting of electric and magnetic fields on a RADIO ANTENNA or transmission line; (2) SOUND, or air-pressure waves, in the tubing of a musical instrument; (3) *mechanical*, regions of tension and relaxation on a vibrating wire or in an enclosed body of liquid. Because the appearance of standing waves implies a precise relationship between the physical dimensions of the system and the wavelength, this effect is of wide use in studying, measuring, and using all kinds of waves.   C. F. R.

Staphylococcus see Bacteriology

Standing waves may appear in a bowl of water in contact with vibrating machine

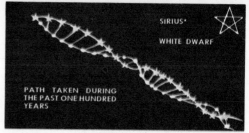

Double star system

Star, double Many of the stars that one sees as points of light are not single stars. Some of them are two, three, four or even six stars revolving around each other. These multiple star systems are held together by the attraction of their gravities. The two-star systems are called *double stars* or *binary* stars. Astronomers have discovered over 25,000 double stars.

Although double stars appear as one star to the naked eye, many doubles can be separated by using binoculars or small telescopes. Very powerful telescopes are needed to separate other double stars. Some doubles are so close together that only the *spectroscope* reveals them to be two stars. The center star in the handle of the *Big Dipper (Ursa Major)* is a double star. It can be observed as two stars through a small telescope.

Double stars are very interesting and often beautiful objects to observe with the telescope. The companions are sometimes very different from each other in size and color. The double in Ursa Major consists of two white stars. *Beta Orionis,* the bright star below and to the right of Orion's belt, is a large white star with a small blue companion. *Antares,* the brightest star in SCORPIUS, is a large red star with a small green companion.   C. L. K.

SEE ALSO: CONSTELLATION, DOPPLER EFFECT, STARS

Star, variable Some stars do not always shine with the same degree of brightness. Stars that vary in the intensity of their brightness are called variable stars. There are over 20,000 known variables. They do not all vary for the same reason.

Some variable stars are *binary* variables. They are double stars, stars that are revolving around each other, and can thus alternately eclipse each other. This causes

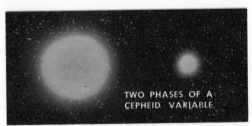
TWO PHASES OF A CEPHEID VARIABLE

Many stars vary in brightness

Buchsbaum
Brittle star

the point of light that is seen as one star to change in brightness.

Other variable stars are single stars called *intrinsic variables*. They change in brightness for different reasons. They seem to pulsate. Some of them have a regular rhythm of variation; some have very irregular rhythms. Some complete their cycles of variation in a few days; others take years to complete a cycle. BETELGEUSE (*Alpha Orionis*) is an irregular intrinsic variable.

A certain type of variable star is called a *Cepheid* variable. The study of the variations of these stars can tell astronomers how far the star is from earth. *Delta Cepheus* was the first star of this type to be discovered.

Novae and supernovae stars have bursts of brightness and then become faint. C. L. K.
SEE ALSO: CONSTELLATION, NOVA, STARS

Starch Starch is a substance stored in plants for food. This material is also eaten and digested by man when he uses various fruits and vegetables for his food. Starch from corn is used in the laundry and in prepared drugs.

In structure, starch is similar to CELLULOSE. Both are made up of repeating molecular units of the simple sugars such as glucose. Starch, however, is digestible by man; cellulose is not. The two general types of starch in nature are called *amylose* and *amylopectin*. Amylose, the smaller molecule, has a molecular weight of about 50,000, and amylopectin has about 300,000. M. S.
SEE ALSO: PLANTS, CHARACTERISTICS OF; SUGAR

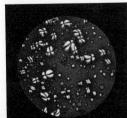

Photo-micrographs by
National Teaching Aids, Inc.
Starch grains

Starfish Starfish are not really fish. They belong to a different group called *echinoderms*. They are also called *sea stars*. A sea star's body is a central circle with arms going out in all directions. Most sea stars have five arms. Some, however, have no arms, whereas others may have from four to fifty. Most starfish are only a few inches across. They eat clams, oysters, and mussels. They are able to eject, or throw out, their stomach to cover and digest the soft parts of these animals. The stomach is then returned to place. This eating habit is not found in any other animal that scientists have discovered.

Starfish, or sea stars, have an *endoskeleton* composed of *calcareous* plates embedded in the flesh. They are covered with short rough spines. Even with this apparent armor, they are quite flexible as they bend and twist. The plates are joined by connective tissue and not fused as in many other animals of the phylum.

Starfish possess a WATER VASCULAR SYSTEM. Water is forced into the many rows of tube feet. Suckers on the ends of them enable the animal to attach itself. They can exert a seven-pound pressure on a closed clam. The starfish's endurance outlasts that of the clam's. The stomach of the starfish can get into the narrowest crack. Excretion is rarely necessary, since the animal predigests the food.

Respiration occurs through short filaments on the dorsal side. They act as gills and are protected by pincers (*pedicellariae*). Three central nerve rings send nerves out to each arm. Special tube feet at the end of each arm are used for smelling. The adjoining eyespot distinguishes light from dark.

The *larvae* of the sea stars are bilaterally symmetrical. This is significant when one traces the progression of animals. The adult becomes radially symmetrical. Each arm has two pairs of *gonads*. The *gametes* are fertilized in the water. Sea stars are able to grow missing parts (*regeneration*). Before the oyster farmers understood the regenerative powers of sea stars, they removed hundreds of animals from oyster beds, placed them on the dock, and chopped them into pieces. These were thrown back into the water. Soon the pieces regenerated into whole animals and the oysters were attacked by thousands of hungry predators.

Brittle stars, shaped like the starfish, belong to another class of echinoderms. Arms are more sharply distinguished from the central disk. Tube feet are sensory.   H. J. C.

SEE ALSO: ECHINODERMATA

Starling The starling is a large, all-black bird. It is the only one with a yellow bill. It has a shorter tail than blackbirds, crows, and grackles. The 60 species of starlings are found all over the world except in the Australian area. The only species in the United States was introduced in 1890 and has become common. It occurs from the East Coast west to the Rocky Mountains and is most abundant in New York State, where it was introduced.

During the winter, starling plumage becomes speckled with white and the bill darkens. The summer plumage has a metallic sheen and its long, pointed bill is yellow. These birds walk instead of hop.

Nests are made of twigs and grasses and are built in hollow trees or building crevices. Starlings are among the first birds to nest in the spring, laying four to six pale-blue eggs. After the breeding season, young and old birds form large flocks.   J. C. K.

Starling

Stars On a clear dark night thousands of tiny points of light polka-dot the sky. Most of these white dots in the black sky are stars. A few of them are planets, shining by reflected light from the sun. On some nights a point of light seems to race across the sky, leaving a blazing trail behind it. This is sometimes called a "shooting star" but it is really a meteor. The rest of the shining dots are stars.

One star can be seen in the daytime. It is the closest star to the earth, the sun. All the other stars are much like the sun. Some are larger; some, smaller. Some are hotter; some, cooler. Some have companion stars. But all stars, like the sun, make their own light and heat.

Even without a telescope, when the air is clear and there is no moon, one can see about 3,000 stars. With a powerful telescope one can see millions of millions of stars. Stars which are relatively close together are in the same *galaxy*. Each galaxy contains thousands of millions of stars, as well as clouds of stellar dust or gas—the *nebulae*. The MILKY WAY is so bright because it is part of the solar galaxy. The sun (and its solar system) is located on one of the arms of a spiral galaxy. Galaxies seem to occur in clusters. Modern observations of the UNIVERSE indicate that each galaxy is receding from every other galaxy at a tremendous speed—the so-called *expanding* universe. It is only because intergalactic, and interstellar, distances are so vast that the galaxies do not appear to the casual observer to be receding.

The sun, the closest star, is 93 million miles away. The other stars are so far away that their distances from Earth are not measured in miles. Star distances are measured in *light years*. When astronomers say that the closest star (besides the sun) is 4¼ light years from earth, they mean that light takes 4¼ years to travel from that star (*Proxima Centauri*) to the earth. And light travels 186,000 miles per second! The light that comes from the Andromeda

A view toward the center of the Milky Way galaxy discloses countless pinpoints of light that are the stars of many types and sizes. The brightest stars might be ten to one thousand light years away. The faint specks that make up the band of the Milky Way could be about ten thousand light years away

galaxy left those stars almost two million years ago. If a star in that group were to blow up suddenly today, astronomers would not know about it for almost two million years.

Proxima Centauri is not bright enough to be seen without a telescope. Some very bright stars seem dim because they are so far away. The brightness of stars is measured in "magnitudes." The brightest stars are "first magnitude." The stars that are

2½ times less bright are second magnitude, and so on. Stars down to the sixth magnitude can be seen with the eye.

Astronomers need a way of classifying a star which does not depend upon the brightness, which varies with distance from the earth. If the light from a star passes through a spectroscope, the light is broken up into a great number of different colors, just as white light passing through a prism is broken up into its constituent colors.

TWENTY BRIGHTEST STARS			
NAME	CONSTELLATION	MAGNITUDE	DISTANCE (LIGHT-YEARS)
Sirius	Canis Major	—1.43	8.6
Canopus	Carina	—0.73	200
Alpha Centauri	Centaurus	—0.27	4
Arcturus	Boötes	—0.06	36
Vega	Lyrae	0.04	26.5
Capella	Auriga	0.09	47
Rigel	Orion	0.15	540
Procyon	Canis Minor	0.37	10.3
Achernar	Eridani	0.53	66
Betelgeuse	Orion	variable	520
Agena	Centaurus	0.66	300
Altair	Aquila	0.80	16.5
Aldebaran	Taurus	0.85	57
Alpha Cruci	Crux	0.87	230
Antares	Scorpius	0.98	360
Spica	Virgo	1.00	230
Fomalhaut	Pisces Australis	1.16	24
Pollux	Gemini	1.16	32
Deneb	Cygnus	1.26	650
Beta Cruci	Crux	1.31	200
Regulus	Leo	1.36	56

These color *lines* indicate what materials are present in the star. Star classification today is largely based on these spectral lines. B stars, for example, have surface temperatures up to 25,000° F, and are known as *helium stars* because HELIUM is very prominent in their spectra. G stars, also known as *solar stars* because they are like the sun, have strong lines due to the presence of metals. N stars are often called *carbon stars* because the carbon lines are so prominent.

The sun is an average-sized star, though it is so near that it seems very large. The *giant stars* are larger than a million suns. Astronomers say that if the supergiant in *Epsilon Aurigae* were to be moved so that its center was at the center of the sun, it would extend beyond the orbit of Saturn.

Stars range in color from orange, to red, to yellow, to white, to blue-white, and green-white. The orange-red stars are coolest, about 3,000° F. The green-white stars are hottest, about 50,000° F, surface temperature. The interior of any star is much hotter than its surface. The general rule is: the deeper in, the higher the temperature.

Astronomers believe that the size, color, heat, and composition of a star tells something of its age. They believe that stars were formed out of clouds of interstellar gas. The GAS collects and starts to condense. As the atoms get closer together, the center heats up and nuclear reactions begin. The heat and light of most stars comes from the NUCLEAR ENERGY released in the conversion of hydrogen into helium.

Once nuclear reaction starts, the star stops its rapid shrinking and is now a so-called *Main Sequence* star. The term *Main Sequence* comes from the formerly accepted theory of stellar evolution which held that stars which had reached the peak of their brilliance (green-white) then became a less energetic white, then a yellow dwarf (like the sun), and finally a red dwarf. Any star in these stages is termed a Main Sequence star, though the theory has been discarded.

Once all the HYDROGEN within the star has been converted to helium, the star must leave the Main Sequence. The helium core starts shrinking. Once 1/10 of the stellar mass is in the core, however, the outer layers of the star suddenly expand tremendously, cooling during expansion. The star becomes a *red giant,* with a small, very hot, very dense core surrounded by a huge cloud of rarefied gas. When the giant star has exhausted all its nuclear power, its structure alters once more and it becomes a very dense so-called *white dwarf.* A white dwarf can evolve no longer; it can radiate only feebly until the last of its energy is dissipated. The sun has just started on the Main Sequence and is growing more luminous all the time. It will be about 10 thousand million years before the sun becomes a white dwarf.   C. L. K.

SEE ALSO: ASTRONOMY, CONSTELLATION, INTERSTELLAR COMMUNICATION, MAGNITUDE, NOVA, SPECTROSCOPE, SUN

Starvation see Malnutrition

States of matter see Gas, Liquid, Physical states and changes

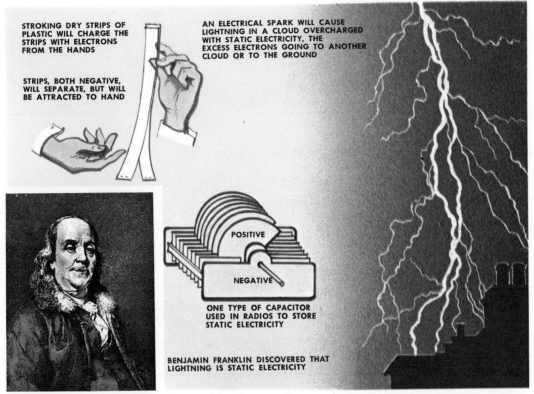

STROKING DRY STRIPS OF PLASTIC WILL CHARGE THE STRIPS WITH ELECTRONS FROM THE HANDS

STRIPS, BOTH NEGATIVE, WILL SEPARATE, BUT WILL BE ATTRACTED TO HAND

AN ELECTRICAL SPARK WILL CAUSE LIGHTNING IN A CLOUD OVERCHARGED WITH STATIC ELECTRICITY, THE EXCESS ELECTRONS GOING TO ANOTHER CLOUD OR TO THE GROUND

POSITIVE

NEGATIVE

ONE TYPE OF CAPACITOR USED IN RADIOS TO STORE STATIC ELECTRICITY

BENJAMIN FRANKLIN DISCOVERED THAT LIGHTNING IS STATIC ELECTRICITY

Static electricity can be easily demonstrated. Devices producing it are used in electronics

Static electricity When the weather is cold and dry, it is common to receive a shock after walking across a wool rug and then touching a metal door knob. If it is dark, a spark may be seen. Sometimes sparks occur when the hair is combed. These shocks and sparks are caused by static electricity.

About 600 B.C. the Greeks learned that if fur were rubbed on amber, the amber would pick up small pieces of straw and other light objects. In 1733, Robert duFay, a Frenchman, discovered two kinds of electricity now termed *positive* and *negative* electricity. Lightning was drawn down a kite string by BENJAMIN FRANKLIN in 1752. He showed that lightning is a large charge of static electricity.

If a rubber comb is stroked with a piece of wool, the atoms of the rubber comb pick up *electrons* from the atoms of wool. The comb becomes negatively charged, while the wool receives a positive charge. The negatively charged comb will pick up small bits of paper, which have no charge. A balloon rubbed against one's hair becomes negatively charged. The balloon then sticks to the ceiling or wall, which have no charge.

Substances may have a negative or a positive charge, depending upon what they rub. If glass is stroked by silk, the glass becomes positive and the silk negative. If silk is rubbed with rubber, the silk receives a positive charge, whereas the rubber becomes negatively charged.

Natural static electricity has limited practical use. Several toys and lint brushes use static electricity. But the principles of static electricity are important in ELECTRONICS; radio and television sets have many electrostatic *capacitors.*

Static electricity may be a source of danger. Gasoline trucks often drag a chain to ground the static electricity that would otherwise set fire to the fuel vapors. If precautions are not taken to avoid static electricity, dust particles in mines and grain elevators may explode. Hospital operating rooms must use special floors to prevent sparks from igniting the anesthetics. P. F. D.

SEE ALSO: ELECTRICITY

Statics see Dynamics, Mechanics

Statistics (stah-TISS-tiks) Statistics is the science which collects, classifies, analyzes, makes inferences, and interprets numerical facts.

When the study of statistics first began, it was concerned with analysis of topics pertaining to the community or the state. Today statistics applies to the analysis of quantitative information regardless of the source of such information.

An unorganized collection of numbers is usually referred to as *rough,* or *raw, data.* There are various ways in which raw data may be classified. The form most often used is the *frequency distribution,* in which data are collected in accordance with the magnitude of the numbers and the frequency with which these numbers appear. Imagine that a group of 19 first-grade pupils wear shoes of the following sizes: 12, 12½, 10, 11½, 10½, 11, 11, 10½, 12, 11, 11½, 10½, 10½, 11, 10, 11, 10½, 11, 11½. This is how the frequency distribution would look for such data:

(1) Sizes	(2) Tally marks	(3) Frequency	(4) Sum
10	//	2	20.0
10½	/////	5	52.5
11	//////	6	66.0
11½	///	3	34.5
12	//	2	24.0
12½	/	1	12.5
		19	209.5

Here is the same data in the form of a column diagram, or *histogram:*

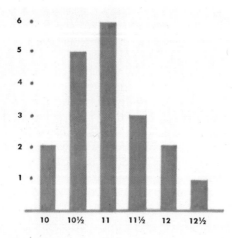

Here is the same data in the form of a *frequency curve:*

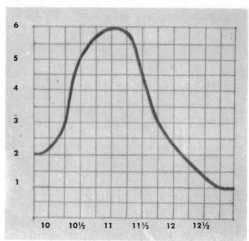

A frequency curve is obtained by first joining the tops of each column in a histogram. This is a *frequency polygon.* The lines of the polygon are smoothed out in a free-hand curve. The weights of many persons, the number of times "heads" appears in each toss of 10 coins over a large number of tosses, the heights of all men in the armed services, etc., give frequency curves approaching theoretically, at least, the bell-shaped curve known as the *normal distribution* (or *Gaussian*) curve.

An *average* gives information about the clustering of a collection of numbers. However, three distinct kinds of averages are used. These are the arithmetic mean, the median, and the mode.

The *arithmetic average,* or *mean,* of a set of numbers is the sum of all the numbers divided by the number of numbers. For the data given in the table above, the mean can be found as follows:

$$M = \frac{209.5}{19}, \text{ or } 11.03.$$

The *median* is the middle, or center, number when all the numbers are arranged according to size. For the data previously given, the median can be computed as follows: Since there are 19 numbers in all, we seek the 10th number. Up to 10½ there are seven cases; three more would bring it exactly to size 11 because one assumes that the six scores contained in interval 11 are evenly distributed in that interval. Therefore size 11 is the median for this particular series.

Observe that six children wore size 11

shoes. This was the most common size. Therefore, the *mode* of this set of numbers was 11 because this was the number that occurred most frequently in the set.

In more advanced treatments on statistics, criteria are given which help the investigator decide which average best suits his purpose.

Measures which describe the scattering, or spread, of a set of numbers are called *measures of dispersion*. The standard deviation for a set of numbers, represented by the symbol σ (sigma), is the most commonly used measure of dispersion. Within 1σ either side of the mean, approximately 68% of all the numbers will be found; more than 95% within 2σ; more than 99% will be found within 3σ.

Statisticians are greatly concerned about statistical inference—predicting with a high degree of accuracy the behavior of a collection of numerical elements from a careful examination of a small sample of these elements. This is an inductive process—reasoning from the particular to the general—and can be erroneous if not thoroughly understood. Statisticians want to be able to make correct inferences. Thus, the accomplished statistician should be an expert in the mathematical theory of probability. There already exist statistical techniques for testing an hypothesis, for analyzing trends, and for comparing two groups of data; but new needs require new statistical methods and these must be developed by the mathematician. I. K. F.

SEE ALSO: MATHEMATICS, PROBABILITY

Steam Steam is a gas form of water. Ice is the solid. Steam is sometimes called *water vapor*. When steam is sealed in a container it contains a great amount of pressure because it occupies 1800 times the space that the water which forms it does. This makes it useful for doing work.

The white cloud visible above boiling water is often mistakenly called steam. It is actually tiny water droplets condensed from the steam.

Since water gas, or vapor, is steam, it could be said that steam is rising from a goldfish bowl in an ordinary room. Although evaporation goes on at room temperature

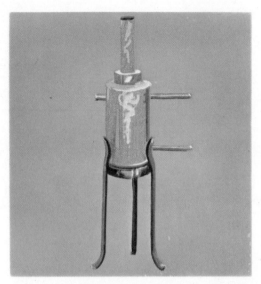

Steam for laboratory experiments is provided by this steam generator

and even below room temperature, this is not steam. Steam is defined as water gas that is evaporated from boiling water, and thus it has a similarly high temperature. Boiling, or rapid evaporation of water normally occurs at 212° F at sea level (15 lbs. pressure).

Steam at the same temperature as the boiling water is saturated steam. If it is heated to a higher temperature, it expands, or tries to expand, even more. This steam is called *superheated* steam. It can be heated to very high temperatures, thus expanding and creating high pressure, if confined, which can be harnessed for great amounts of work.

Over five times the energy is required to change boiling water to steam than to raise an equal amount from freezing to boiling (32-212°). This energy is called *latent heat,* which is retained until the steam condenses back to water.

Steam (superheated) is used for transferring heat energy in heating systems, especially where the boiler is distant from where the heat is required. It is, of course, used in steam engines, especially in the turbine. D. J. I.

SEE ALSO: ENERGY, EVAPORATION

Steam engine see Engine; Train, railroad; Turbine

Steam turbine see Turbine

Steamboat see Fulton, Robert

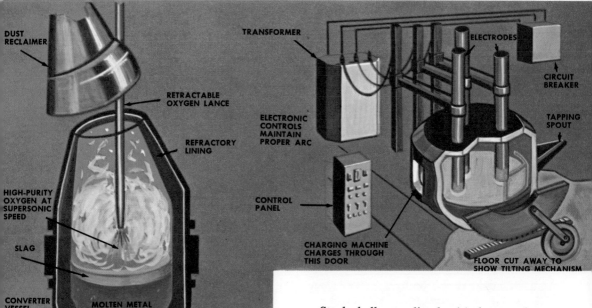

Oxygen convertor

Labels on diagram:
DUST RECLAIMER
RETRACTABLE OXYGEN LANCE
REFRACTORY LINING
HIGH-PURITY OXYGEN AT SUPERSONIC SPEED
SLAG
CONVERTER VESSEL
MOLTEN METAL BATH
TRANSFORMER
ELECTRODES
CIRCUIT BREAKER
TAPPING SPOUT
ELECTRONIC CONTROLS MAINTAIN PROPER ARC
CONTROL PANEL
CHARGING MACHINE CHARGES THROUGH THIS DOOR
FLOOR CUT AWAY TO SHOW TILTING MECHANISM

Steel Steel is a mixture, or alloy, of the element iron with certain other minerals. Steel is stronger and tougher than the other forms of man-made iron. The great strength of the different kinds of modern steel comes from the removal of extra carbon from the crude iron and from the addition of special elements, such as *manganese, nickel,* and *chromium.* Also, special ways of heating, cooling, and working the ALLOY result in steels of qualities fitted to many modern needs.

There are several methods for making steel from scrap iron and pig iron. They include the open-hearth process, the Bessemer process, and the oxygen-convertor process.

ELECTRIC FURNACE PROCESS

When exacting alloy steels are required, such as in missiles, rockets, and tools, the electric furnace process is used. Stainless steel is made by this process. These uses comprise about seven per cent of steel used. The quality of the steel produced can be carefully controlled in the electric furnace process.

Steel shells are lined with heat resistant bricks. The *electrodes,* which are large sticks of CARBON, extend from the roof of the furnace down into the metal. High-voltage current is turned on and an electric arc forms between the carbon electrodes, providing a temperature of 3500°. Raw materials for electric furnaces may consist entirely of scrap steel, although open hearth, or other steels, may be used and thus further refined. Alloy steel is made by adding appropriate amounts of chromium, nickel, tungsten, or other ferroalloys to produce different qualities as desired.

THE OXYGEN-CONVERTER PROCESS

Until quite recently, most steel was made by the open-hearth method. This method could produce high-quality steel on a mass-production basis. As new furnaces have been needed, this process has been set aside in favor of the quicker, more economical, and more readily controllable oxygen-convertor process.

In 1955, the Linz-Donawitz oxygen convertor process was begun in Austria, and adaptations of it have spread to Canada and the United States. Like the turbohearth furnace, the oxygen convertor uses newly-available, cheaply-produced pure oxygen as its fuel. The oxygen convertor is considered by metallurgical scientists to be the forerunner of a revolution in steelmaking.

The oxygen convertor is similar in shape to the Bessemer convertor and uses high-purity oxygen which is blown in at supersonic speed. The time for heating and oxidizing one charge is very short—about 20 minutes—as in the Bessemer process.

Basic Steelmaking Steps

1 Making Iron

TWO TONS OF IRON ORE, ONE TON OF COKE AND ONE-HALF TON OF LIME-STONE, TO WHICH FOUR TONS OF AIR IS ADDED, MELTED IN A BLAST FURNACE AT 3,000 DEGREES FAHRENHEIT, PRODUCES IRON.

IRON ORE   COKE   LIMESTON

2 Making Steel

STEEL

IRON

SCRA

ONE PART IRON AND ONE PART SCRAP, COOKE IN AN OPEN HEARTH UNTIL THE MIXTURE MELTS MAKES STEEL

3 Rolling Steel

ROLLED STEEL IS MADE FROM A SOLID INGOT OF STEEL, RUN BE-TWEEN TWO GIANT ROLLS

ROLLS

All pictures courtesy Inland Steel

(Upper left) Blast furnace. Raw materials are poured from the top, to be heated at 3000° F. for a period of four to five hours. Finished product (steel) is removed from the bottom of the blast furnace in ladle cars. The liquid steel is poured into molds to form ingots

(Center left) The ingots are then stripped of the mold and carefully placed in a deep furnace called the *soaking pit*. This furnace keeps the ingots at temperatures to permit rolling

(Lower left) Hot strip rolling converts steel slabs to sheets (3/16″ or less) or plate (1/4″ or more), by a system of synchronized rollers, pressing the slab to desired thickness

TYPES OF STEEL

Hundreds of kinds of steel are produced to meet the varying demands of industry, national defense, and Space Age vehicles. These may be classified in three groups:

1. Carbon steels are most widely used in structural parts of buildings, farm equipment, and bridges.

2. Alloy steels are used where there is the need for extra hardness; rust, acid, and heat resistance; high tensile strength or high ductility; and low rate of heat expansion.

3. Tool steels, which are made using carbon and certain other metals as alloying agents with iron, give tools sufficient hardness and tensile strength.   E. Y. K.

SEE ALSO: BESSEMER PROCESS, IRON, METAL, OPEN HEARTH PROCESS

Stele of carrot cross section

Stele (STEE-lee) When the root of a carrot is cut across, two rings can be seen. The bright orange outer circle surrounds the yellow core, or stele. The cells in the stele carry material up and down the plant.

The stele is a central cylinder found only in the roots and stems of the higher plants. It is composed of vascular tissue. *Xylem* cells transport raw material up to the leaves, and *phloem* cells take the manufactured food down to root tips. The stele may also have strengthening cells for support, such as *pericycle* fibers.   H. J. C.

SEE ALSO: ROOT, STEM, VASCULAR BUNDLE

Stellar (STEHL-ahr) Stellar means having to do with the stars or resembling a star in shape, brightness, or some other way.

SEE: ASTRONOMY, STARS

Stem A stem is the part of a plant that grows up from the roots. LEAVES and flowers grow on the stem. Stems are usually round. Their main job is to support the leaves and to conduct raw materials up from the roots. Some stems are green and can make food. Underground stems store food, as in the case of the white potato.

Leaves, flowers, and branches grow from stems at certain places called *nodes*. Little pores or *lenticels* on the outside of the stem permit the exchange of gases. As a leaf falls off it leaves a leaf scar. The growth at the terminal bud slows down as winter approaches and leaves an ANNUAL RING. Lateral buds grow into branches which give dicots (maple, oak) their spreading appearance. Most of the growth of MONOCOTYLEDONS (palms) is from the terminal bud.

Stems are classified according to their internal structure. The stems of monocots contain scattered vascular bundles, very pithy, usually no bark or secondary growth. DICOTYLEDONS have the vascular bundles arranged in circles, develop bark usually in the third year. The older wood in the center of a stem becomes clogged and is called HEARTWOOD. The outer ring of cells are conducting. This is called SAPWOOD.

Economically stems are very valuable to man. He gets maple syrup, latex for rubber, cork, medicinal juices, lumber, paper, fibers, food, and other products from the cells or cellular secretions of stems.   I. H. S.

SEE ALSO: PLANT

Stem, underground Some plants have stems which grow underground. Leaves develop from the stem and grow upward, and roots sprout and grow down, just as in stems which grow above ground. Such stems hold the food supply, and are called *rhizomes, tubers, bulbs,* or *corms*.

The thick, fleshy, underground parts of the iris plant are rhizomes. Rhizomes usually grow horizontally and are perennial, living from year to year. They have nodes where green, scalelike leaves bud. Rhizomes of quack grass are long and slender. Rhi-

Cactus stores water in its pulpy stems

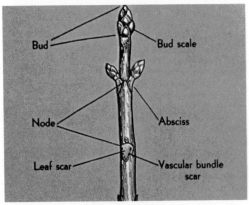

External stem

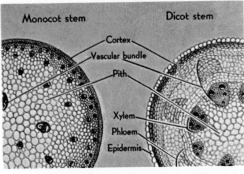

Above pictures Courtesy Society For Visual Education, Inc.

Internal stem (monocot left, dicot right)

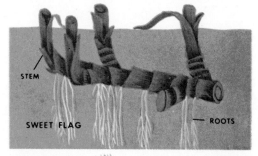

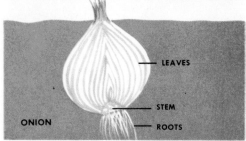

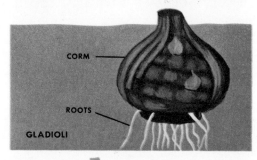

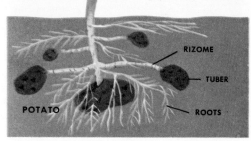

zomes of the canna, sweet flag, and water lily are thick.

Tubers, such as the POTATO are swollen ends of rhizomes. Tubers have eyes scattered over the surface which contain a miniature leaf and usually three buds. This leaf and its buds correspond to the leaf and bud of a stem that grows above ground. A scar can be seen on a tuber showing where it was attached to the rhizome.

A BULB is a very short underground stem surrounded by thick, fleshy leaves which are called bulb scales. The plant's food is stored in the scales. When an onion, which is a bulb, is cut in half, the layers, or series of rings in the scales, can be seen. The scales of most lily bulbs are small and loosely attached to the stem instead of encircling it. DAFFODILS, HYACINTHS, SNOWDROPS, and TULIPS are early spring flowers that grow from bulbs.

A corm is an underground stem with flower and leaf shoots at the top. The corm is covered by scale leaves. The corm holding the food shrivels as the food is used by the plant. The base of the stem enlarges, and a new corm forms on top of the old. *Gladioli* and *crocuses* form corms. P. G. B.

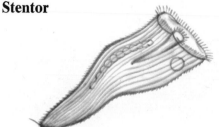

Stentors are tiny animals

Stentor (STENN-tawr) These are single-celled animals covered by hairlike fibers called CILIA. They may be free-swimming or attached to something else. When swimming they are oval and they become trumpet-shaped when attached. There are two common species —one is bluish, while the other is green because small green algae live in its interior (*endoplasm*). Swimming is done by the cilia. When attached, the cell can be shortened by *contractile fibrils*.

Around the mouth or aboral end, cilia are flattened and called *membranelles*. The mouth or *cytosome* opens into an *oral chamber* or passageway containing an *undulating membrane* made of fused cilia. At the base of this chamber is a *cytopharynx,* which has no cilia. Food that has been swept in by the membranelles and undulating membrane is enclosed in a vacuole, circulated through the cytoplasm, and digested. Food consists of dead and living organic material. Digestive waste is eliminated through a pore near the mouth.

Reproduction is asexual, by transverse fission. The long chainlike macronucleus rounds up and each micronucleus forms a spindle.

J. C. K.

SEE ALSO: CILIA, PROTOZOA

Steppe (STEP) A steppe is a region that is created by the climatic conditions that result in the natural growth of grasses and shrubs. Steppes are semiarid (have little rainfall). They are found in the middle latitudes as well as in the tropics.

SEE ALSO: ASIA, CLIMATE

Steradian see Candela

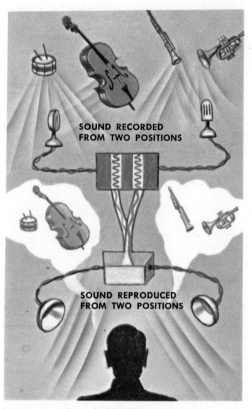

Stereo recording holds the sounds of each instrument in its own space and is heard by the listener with both ears, or binaurally

Stereophonic sound Sounds in stereo are recorded from two or more positions simultaneously. The reproduction of the sound by two or more systems of speakers properly spaced gives the listener the directional effect of his "binaural" hearing.

SEE: RADIO, SOUND RECORDING

Stereoscope A stereoscope is an instrument through which two pictures printed side by side are viewed, one with each eye, giving the appearance of a single 3-dimensional image.

Sterility (stuh-RILL-ih-tee) Sterility refers to the inability of plants or animals to reproduce their kind. Sterility may result from defective reproductive organs, glandular disturbances, poor health, extreme temperatures, excessive radiation, or genetic causes.

Sterilization (stair-uh-luh-ZA-shun)

Sterilization is a process by which very tiny bacteria, called *germs,* are destroyed. They may be destroyed by various forms of heat or chemicals. It is very important to kill harmful bacteria in hospitals and offices of physicians so that disease will be prevented from spreading.

Joseph Lister, an English surgeon, is credited with starting the use of sterilization in surgery. This was a practical development of Louis Pasteur's theory that infection is caused by bacteria. This technique of keeping germs out was termed *aseptic surgery.* He had great success with asepsis. There was an important decrease in fatalities from bacterial infection among surgical patients.

Sterilization of instruments is important because it prevents infection from reaching a wound.

There are several effective methods of sterilization. Fire (or ovens) is often used to sterilize durable items, such as needles in a home and glassware in hospitals. In the offices of physicians and in hospitals an *autoclave,* or steam-heated cabinet, is used. The use of heated air is necessary to sterilize medicines that are oily.

Another method of partial sterilization is pasteurization. In this process, a substance such as milk is heated to a temperature which kills the bacteria, but does not spoil the milk.

D. E. Z.

SEE ALSO: PASTEURIZATION; LISTER, JOSEPH

Sternum   see Skeleton

Steroid (STAIR-oyd)

Steroids are a group of related chemical substances found in all plant and animal cells. These complex compounds include sterols, bile acids, sex hormones, adrenal hormones, and some substances that produce cancer.

CHOLESTEROL is the best known animal steroid. It is found in large amounts in nerve tissue and in gallstones. *Ergosterol* is found in the skin of animals. The ultraviolet rays of sunlight change ergosterol into vitamin D, which prevents rickets, a crippling disease. The three types of sex hormones—

BASIC STEROID STRUCTURE

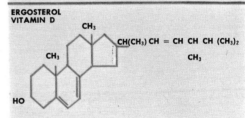

CHOLESTEROL

ERGOSTEROL VITAMIN D

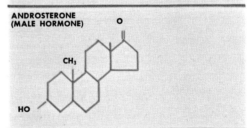

ANDROSTERONE (MALE HORMONE)

ESTRONE (FEMALE HORMONE)

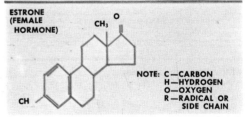

NOTE: C—CARBON
H—HYDROGEN
O—OXYGEN
R—RADICAL OR SIDE CHAIN

Chemical structure of some steroids

androgens, estrogens, and *progesterones*— and the adrenal cortical hormones, *corticosterones* are steroids. The bile acids, *cholic acid* and related acids, are steroids that digest fat.

Sitosterol is the most widely distributed plant sterol. It is closely related to cholesterol. Animals make steroids within their bodies and are unable to use as food the steroids produced by plants.   B. B. G.

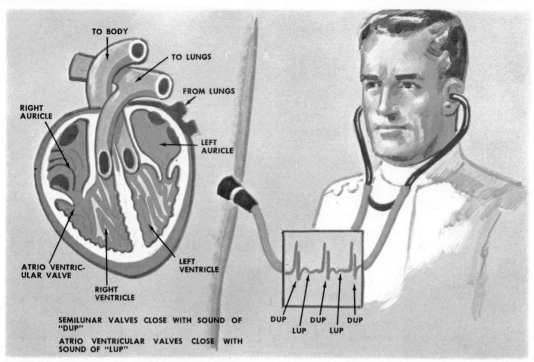

TO BODY

TO LUNGS

FROM LUNGS

RIGHT AURICLE

LEFT AURICLE

ATRIO VENTRIC-ULAR VALVE

LEFT VENTRICLE

RIGHT VENTRICLE

SEMILUNAR VALVES CLOSE WITH SOUND OF "DUP"

ATRIO VENTRICULAR VALVES CLOSE WITH SOUND OF "LUP"

DUP   DUP   DUP
    LUP   LUP

Sounds from within the body made by the heart and other organs are heard with a stethoscope

Stethoscope (STEHTH-oh-skope) The stethoscope is a device used by physicians for listening to sounds coming from within the body. Physicians can determine whether sounds produced by parts of the body represent normal or abnormal conditions. The beats of the HEART, or sounds in the lungs or intestines, are commonly checked by means of the stethoscope.

The usual stethoscope is constructed with two pear-shaped parts that fit into the examiner's ears. Attached are short pipes and rubber tubes which lead to a cone or small, round, boxlike part, which is placed on the body. Sounds are transmitted through the tubes to the physician's ears.   D. J. I.

Stickleback Sticklebacks are small, fierce fish. They live in cool and temperate waters of the Northern Hemisphere. They have several spines along their backs. Instead of scales, they have bony plates, or *scutes,* on their bodies. They are from one to six or seven inches long.

The male sticklebacks do most of the work of preparing and caring for the young. The father builds a nest of weeds cemented together with a sticky, thread-like secretion from his kidneys. Then, he coaxes or forces several females into the nest, one at a time, to lay eggs. He fertilizes the eggs, guards them, and sees that fresh water flows through the nest. Some sticklebacks fan water through the nest with their tails. Some build nests several "stories" high. When the eggs hatch, the father stands guard and tries to keep the young fish home until they are grown up.

Some species live in fresh water; some in salt water; some can live in either. The 12 or 13 species are also different in the number of spines—from two to about ten.   C. L. K.

Stickleback

Stigma In a flower, the stigma is the often knobbed end of the PISTIL, or female part. It receives the pollen during POLLINATION.
SEE: FLOWER

Still see Distillation

Stimulant (STIHM-you-lunt) A stimulant is an agent, such as CAFFEINE or adrenalin, which temporarily quickens activity either in some organ or in the whole body. Stimulants act upon the NERVOUS SYSTEM to speed up action in the other systems.

Stimulus (STIMM-yuh-luhs) Any change that happens near, or inside, a living thing that affects a sense organ is a stimulus. Stimuli (plural) usually lead the living thing to perform some action or response. For example, if a light is shined into a person's eye, the light beam is a stimulus. The narrowing of the pupil of the person's eye is the usually observed response.

Any sort of physical change can act as a stimulus. When one accidentally touches a hot stove, the change is obvious. But a stimulus can be the removal of some force, such as the lightening of pressure of a tight shoelace.

In man and in higher animals, stimuli are detected by sense organs. These sense receptors, in turn, send impulses along the nerves to the spinal cord, and perhaps also to the brain.

Stimuli and their effects are studied by special biologists who work in *physiology* and *psychology*.   D. J. I.
SEE ALSO: NERVOUS SYSTEM

Sting ray see Ray

Stinkbug see Bugs

Stock see Grafting

Stomach see Digestive system, Ruminant

Stomata see Leaves, Transpiration

Stone see Gallstone, Rocks

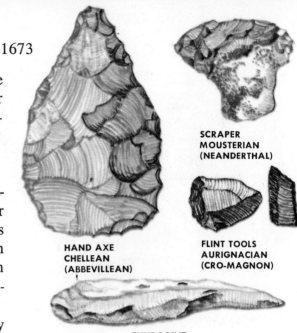

SCRAPER
MOUSTERIAN
(NEANDERTHAL)

HAND AXE
CHELLEAN
(ABBEVILLEAN)

FLINT TOOLS
AURIGNACIAN
(CRO-MAGNON)

FLINT POINT
SOLUTREAN
(CRO-MAGNON)

Paleolithic stone artifacts

Stone Age The Stone Age covers those times before the discovery of metal when man, or his manlike ancestors, used stone for tools.

The Stone Age is usually divided into four eras: *Eolithic* (Dawn Stone Age); *Paleolithic* (Old Stone Age); *Mesolithic* (Middle Stone Age); and *Neolithic* (New Stone Age). The Paleolithic is divided into Lower, Middle, and Upper Paleolithic. Each of these ages is further subdivided according to cultures of the time.

The Stone Age in Europe existed during the Ice Ages when the great glaciers swept down from the north. Some of the Stone Age peoples seem to have come from Africa or Asia, moving out to cover Europe and, sometimes, retreating before the glaciers. Egypt and the Indus Valley in India had complex metal-working civilizations almost 10,000 years before Europe entered the Bronze Age. The Bronze Age is the period before the discovery of iron when copper and tin were smelted to make the alloy bronze. Since much of the investigation of Stone Age cultures has been done in western Europe, all correlation of cultures to dates and geological eras refers to western Europe. Similar cultures may have arisen in different areas of the world at other times.

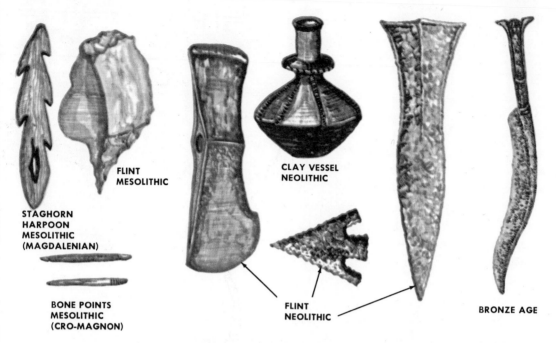

FLINT
MESOLITHIC

CLAY VESSEL
NEOLITHIC

STAGHORN
HARPOON
MESOLITHIC
(MAGDALENIAN)

BONE POINTS
MESOLITHIC
(CRO-MAGNON)

FLINT
NEOLITHIC

BRONZE AGE

Artifacts from the Mesolithic, Neolithic and the beginning of the Bronze Age

Very little is known about life in Eolithic times. Chipped tools of flint, a very hard quartz, have been found; but these objects could have been formed naturally. Eolithic man was probably a nomad, gathering his food by hunting, and not possessing fire.

During the interglacial epochs of the Lower Paleolithic period, man-apes hunted huge elephants, hippopotamuses, rhinoceroses, and saber-toothed tigers. They probably dug a pit and lined it with pointed sticks and, after driving the animal into it, beat it to death with their hand axes. These Chellean (Abbevillean) hand axes were made by knocking flakes off a piece of flint until it took on the required shape. These primitive people of the Lower Paleolithic period also made pottery, which indicates that they probably roasted meat over an open fire. As glaciers covered Europe, the animals gave way to mammoths and the woolly-coated rhinoceroses.

Neanderthal (Mousterian) man developed during the Middle Paleolithic period. He was a careful worker of flake flint tools, which he buried with his dead.

During the Upper Paleolithic period, Cro-Magnon man made his first appearance. This Aurignacian was a cave-dweller, and made scrapers, knives, and carvers of flint. He made tools of bone and ivory which he engraved, and invented the bow and arrow.

He probably invented the bow-drill which helped to make fire. He even painted the walls of his caves and carved statuettes, creating the first art.

The Solutreans seem to have invaded Europe from the East. They developed bone needles and brought flint-flaking to a point never surpassed.

Magdalenian man hunted and developed the harpoon with which he fished in the arctic waters. He developed painting to a high degree, making paints out of natural earths, using reindeer horn as a palette.

During Mesolithic times, the dog was domesticated and used for hunting in the great forests which appeared. Flint was again used for making tools, but worked crudely. Engravings of boats indicate water transportation had developed.

In the Neolithic period, man domesticated animals and began to farm. He wove fibers into cloth; no longer were skins the only form of clothing. He planted grain, and cut, threshed, and ground it into flour, which he baked into unleavened bread in clay ovens. During the Neolithic period the first villages appeared.

In relating the type of man to the type of culture, it is important to remember that the same cultural level was attained by different groups at different times. The Far East may have been in Neolithic times while

STONE AGE CULTURES				
YEARS AGO	GLACIAL STAGE	CULTURAL	TRADITION	CHARACTERISTICS
5000	Postglacial	Neolithic		Agriculture Domestic animals Pottery Boats Weaving
6000	Postglacial	Mesolithic		Dog, domesticated Boats Crude flint tools
10-20,000	Würm glacial	Upper Paleolithic	Magdalenian	Harpoons Fishing Hunting Highly developed paintings
30-20,000	Würm glacial	Upper Paleolithic	Solutrean	Bone needles Flake-flint tools highly developed
50-10,000	Würm glacial	Upper Paleolithic	Aurignacian	Flint scrapers, knives, gravers Bone and ivory tools Bow and arrow Cave paintings
150-100,000	Würm glacial and Third interglacial	Middle Paleolithic	Mousterian (Neanderthal)	Flake flint tools Ceremonial burial
350-150,000	Riss glacial and great interglacial	Lower Paleolithic	Acheulean	Core tools highly developed
600-350,000	Günz glacial First interglacial mindel glacial	Lower Paleolithic	Abbevillean or Chellean	Core tools Fire Food gathering Hunting
— -600,000	Early glacials	Eolithic		Food gathering Hunting No fire Crude flint tools

Europe was in Paleolithic. Thus, cultures may not be dated with great accuracy.

Recent discoveries have linked tools to prehuman primates of almost two million years ago. These creatures did not yet walk completely on two feet. Until these finds were made, it was thought that man developed into a man-like shape and then gained the use of tools. It is now becoming increasingly clear that the structure of man evolved through the use of tools by four-footed primates. The Stone Age, then, is not a purely "human" phenomenon and may be studied apart from man.   J. F. B.

SEE ALSO: EVOLUTION OF MAN, GLACIAL AGES

Storage battery see Battery

Stork

Stork (STAWRK) Most children have seen a picture of the long-legged stork. In North America, however, the true stork is found only in zoos. Its real home is in Europe, Asia, and Africa. The children of Europe are most familiar with the white stork because it nests on chimneys or roof-tops. Every spring, white storks fly north and return to the same nests. They usually keep the same mates, and are very protective of their young. It is considered good luck to have a stork's nest on a house.

The wood *ibis* and *jabiru* are the only stork types found in the Americas, although there are several kinds of true storks in the Old World, the white stork of Europe, the *Marabou* or adjutant of Africa. These birds, some of which stand four feet tall and have broad, footlong beaks, are said to be the only voiceless birds. These wading birds feed on insects, small reptiles, and fish.

J. A. D.

Stork's-bill The stork's-bill (or crane's-bill) is a flowering plant that belongs to the geranium family, with about 700 species. It is characterized by beak-shaped fruit.

Stork's-bill is of the geranium family

Storm A storm is a violent disturbance in the atmosphere. It usually involves a whirling motion of the air and winds, and is often accompanied by rain or other PRECIPITATION. SEE: SQUALL LINE, WEATHER

Strain see Elasticity, Stress

Strait A strait is a channel of water generally narrower than either of the bodies of water it connects. It is usually only a few miles wide, although it might be fairly long. Straits differ from CANALS because they are natural and not man-made.

There are many well-known straits. The *Strait of Gibraltar* connects the Atlantic Ocean and the Mediterranean Sea, separating Spain and Africa. It varies in width from eight to 23 miles. Rocks on either side are called *Pillars of Hercules*.

The *Strait of Mackinac* connects Lakes Michigan and Huron, which lie to the west and east of the Lower Peninsula of Michigan. The Upper Peninsula of the state bounds the north side of the strait, whereas the Lower Peninsula lies on the southern side. It is an important link in the inland water route to the Atlantic. The narrowest width of the Strait of Mackinac, which is five miles across, is spanned by the famous straits bridge.

The *Strait of Magellan* exists between the southern tip of South America and Tierra del Fuego. D. J. I.

Strato-cumulus see Clouds

Stratosphere see Atmosphere

Stratum see Geology, Paleontology

Stratus see Clouds

Strawberry Strawberry is not a plant with a woody stem, so botanists call it an *herb*. Because the plant comes up each spring without replanting, it is a *perennial*. Strawberry plants have three-part leaves and five-petaled, white flowers.

The red fruit is called a BERRY but is not a true berry. The part that is eaten is the base of the flower which grows and becomes

Strawberry plant

juicy and fleshy. The true fruits are on the outside of the fleshy part and are incorrectly called *seeds*.

Strawberries spread by branches called *runners*. These grow on top of the soil forming new plants at the *nodes*. The flower has many pistils, each containing one *ovule*. The ovary of each pistil develops into a dry fruit, an *achene*. Achenes are scattered over the surface of the fleshy, edible flower base (*receptacle*). J. C. K.

SEE ALSO: FRUIT

Strawflower

Strawflower Strawflower is a common name for an annual plant in the *composites*. When the flowers dry, they keep their color and feel like straw.

Stream A stream is a flowing mass of matter, most commonly water. Excess rain that falls gathers in natural streams to form rivers. Some streams are man-made to drain bodies of standing water.

Stream, jet, see Jet stream

Streamlining Streamlining is the process of shaping a body so as to reduce its drag (resistance to air or fluid through which it moves). The body is shaped to conform to the pattern which a fluid follows when it flows steadily, without turbulence.

SEE: AERODYNAMICS

Streptococcus see Bacteria

Streptomycin see Antibiotics

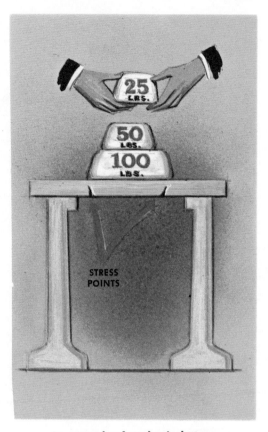
An example of mechanical stress

Stress All objects are acted upon by their environment and respond to the environment in characteristic ways. When the environment changes to one different from normal, this environment acts as a stress on the object. The object responds to this stress by either adjusting to it, or counteracting it, or removing it.

Stresses may be mechanical, electromagnetic, thermal, chemical, bacterial, and so on.

The analysis of mechanical stress is very important in the design of bridges, buildings, towers, machinery, aircraft, and spacecraft. The limiting stress that any structure would be expected to stand up under must be known or guessed, and the structure then designed to withstand or accommodate that stress. A suspension BRIDGE, for example, must be designed so that it does not collapse under the weight of the traffic it will carry, so that it is not torn loose from its moor-

Courtesy Society For Visual Education, Inc.

Astronauts in training are subjected to both physical and psychological stress as they are studied for man's possible reactions during space flights

ings by a high wind, and so that it does not buckle when the heat of the sun makes it expand.

Objects which are relatively simple respond to stresses in simple ways. For example, if an iron wire is pulled, it will stretch; if heated, the wire will get hot; if dipped into a strong chemical, it may dissolve.

BIOLOGICAL STRESS

More highly organized objects, especially living organisms, may respond to stress in very complex ways. For example, if a cat's tail is pulled, it may bite, scratch, squirm, and try to escape. Its heart will beat faster, its blood will circulate more rapidly, it will breathe more deeply, its fur will stand on end.

The complex response of an animal is due to two factors. First, the existence in the animal of several functional systems (respiratory, circulatory, muscular, sensory, nervous, endocrine, etc.) and second, the interconnections of these systems with each other. These systems are so interconnected that they continually make adjustments to counteract the effects of stress. The systems tend toward homeostasis, a condition in which every system is in balance with the demands of both the environment and all the other systems.

When the human body is subjected to stress, the pituitary gland is stimulated to secrete *corticotropin,* which, in turn, stimulates the *adrenal cortex* to produce *corticoid* hormones. The corticoids reduce inflammation and cause the kidney to secrete hormones that affect the *blood pressure.*

Because stress involves the entire body in an intense struggle, many diseases can result. These "diseases of adaptation" include overworking of the pituitary and adrenal glands, often ending in their complete exhaustion and nonfunctioning. Rheumatic diseases, hypertension, kidney disease, fibrous deposits in the blood vessels, diabetes, ulcers, and psychosomatic disorders can be produced by stress.

Dr. Hans Selye, a Canadian physiologist, was a pioneer in the research and theoretical work which make possible an understanding of the effects of biological stress.   B. B. G.

SEE ALSO: ADAPTATION, ADRENAL GLANDS, ELASTICITY, HOMEOSTASIS, PITUITARY, STIMULUS

Strontium (STRAHN-shee-um) The chemical element strontium is a silvery white metal. Its name comes from the town of Strontian in Scotland, where the mineral strontianite was first found.

Commercially valuable deposits of the ore *strontianite* and also of *celestite,* a sulfate of strontium, are now mined mainly in northern England.

The free element is not found in nature. It is prepared by the electrolysis of molten strontium chloride.

Strontium (symbol Sr) has atomic number 38. Its atomic weight is 87.62 (87.63, O = 16) and specific gravity is 2.54. It tarnishes (oxidizes) quickly in moist air and catches fire when heated by friction.

A few strontium compounds have notable uses. Most strontium salts burn with a bright red color when set aflame. Thus they are used in fireworks and signal flares. Strontium hydroxide, $Sr(OH)_2$, is used to remove sugar crystals from crude molasses. Certain other strontium compounds—such as the lactate and the bromide—have medicinal uses. Strontium peroxide is put into tracer bullets, to light up the path of the bullets toward the target.

The main stable ISOTOPES of strontium are Sr^{86} and Sr^{88}. The isotope Sr^{90} is radioactive and emits beta particles (electrons). When a hydrogen BOMB or atomic bomb is exploded, Sr^{90} and many other isotopes are formed. Later, this material falls to Earth as "fallout." By this time, many of the radioactive isotopes have transformed into stable isotopes that are not radioactive. But Sr^{90} has a HALF-LIFE of 28 years; this means that it takes 28 years for half of the Sr^{90} that falls on grass, trees, and plants, and into water to disappear. The ground will be radioactive for years after the explosion. If people eat contaminated plants or if cows eat contaminated grass and people drink milk from the cows, Sr^{90} may get into a person's body. Since strontium chemically is like calcium it is taken up by bone. With a great amount of Sr^{90} in the bone, a person may develop bone cancer or leukemia.

D. A. B.

SEE ALSO: ELEMENTS; RADIATION, BIOLOGICAL EFFECTS OF; RADIOACTIVE ELEMENTS

Strychnine (STRIHK-ninn) Strychnine is a deadly POISON obtained from the coats of seeds of a tree native to India and the East Indies. The tree is often grown in the tropics.

Strychnine is used to poison rodents and vermin. It is also used in medicines in small doses. This drug acts as a respiratory stimulant when the central nervous system is highly depressed, as from extreme doses of alcohol or certain sedatives. V. V. N.

Stucco see Plaster

Chicago Natural History Museum
Lake sturgeon

Sturgeon (STUHR-jun) Sturgeons include both salt-water and lake fishes. The sturgeon's body has bony shields and the head is pointed. Its mouth is toothless, and it eats by sucking in food. Both the flesh and the salted eggs (*caviar*) are eaten.

Several species of sturgeon live in American and Canadian lakes; others inhabit Atlantic coastal waters and migrate up streams. Northern Europe, especially Russia, has important edible species. Some kinds of sturgeons grow to twenty feet long and weigh over a half ton. Besides giving caviar, these sturgeons' white flesh is valued as a smoked delicacy; and the air bladder yields a gelatin called *isinglass,* useful in filtering beverages.

D. A. B.

Sty A sty is an inflamed swelling, like a pimple, on the edge of the *eyelid.* Pus germs that are rubbed on the eyelid cause an infection in the root of the eyelash, and a tiny gland becomes inflamed and swells. When the sty breaks the infection can spread.

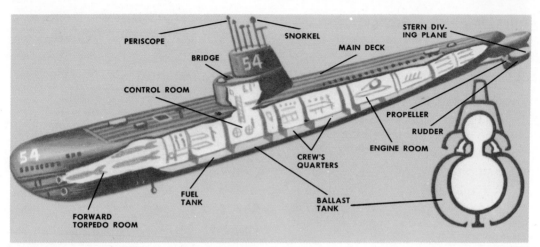

PERISCOPE   SNORKEL   STERN DIV-ING PLANE

BRIDGE   MAIN DECK

CONTROL ROOM

PROPELLER

RUDDER

ENGINE ROOM

CREW'S QUARTERS

FUEL TANK

BALLAST TANK

FORWARD TORPEDO ROOM

Cross-section (right) of a submerged submarine; the ballast tanks are filled with water. To surface, high-pressure air is used to blow out the water

Sublimation (suhb-lih-MAY-shun) Sublimation can also be called *dry evaporation*. This means that a substance on being heated evaporates without first melting.

Every solid has a certain vapor pressure at a particular temperature. This is the pressure due to molecules of the substance escaping from the solid to form a gas. As the temperature increases, the vapor pressure increases. At a high enough temperature, the solid will melt. But if the vapor pressure of a substance is high, a large number of the molecules escape even at temperatures below the melting point of the solid. The solid therefore can evaporate without first being converted to a liquid. This is the case for iodine and sulfur and this fact can be used to purify these substances.   M. S.

SEE ALSO: CHEMISTRY; EVAPORATION

Submarine (SUHB-mah-reen) A submarine is a ship that can travel on or beneath the surface of the water. Submarines were originally used as naval vessels to attack enemy navy and cargo ships. In recent years, many types of nonmilitary submarines have been developed to serve as research vessels. They explore the depths of the sea in connection with the study of OCEANOGRAPHY. The newest submarines have atomic reactors which generate their power supply.

In World Wars I and II, the main weapon of the submarine was the *torpedo,* a miniature submarine powered by electric batteries or compressed air. This weapon carried several hundred pounds of TNT explosive. It proved extremely effective against enemy shipping of all kinds.

All submarines depend on changing their BUOYANCY to submerge and to surface. *Archimedes' principle* states that a floating body displace its own weight in water. A submerged body does not displace enough water to equal its own weight. A submarine can act as either a floating or submerged body, changing its weight by storing sea water in *ballast* tanks. To accomplish this, conventional submarines have double hulls. The outer hull takes most of the pressure strain, whereas the inner hull contains the engines and living quarters. Between the hulls are the ballast and fuel tanks. When the submarine submerges, the main ballast tanks are flooded through quick-opening valves until the ship attains a negative buoyancy. Compressed air forces the water from the ballast tanks to make the submarine surface.

The depth of a moving submarine is controlled employing *hydrodynamic* surfaces, similar to those of an airplane rudder or elevator. The rudder pivots the submarine through horizontal angles by reacting against moving water. Similarly, the elevators (called *diving planes*) move the submarine through vertical angles. When the submarine is moving silently through maximum depths to escape detection by enemy destroyers, its buoyancy must be very delicately adjusted to achieve this neutral buoyancy. The density of water changes very little with depth, so that any slight changes in ballast will cause it either to sink to a dangerous pressure level, or rise to the surface. Usually, silent running submarines maintain a very slow movement with their electric motors, so that they can control their depth easily with the diving planes.

Submarines of the U.S. Fleet Class were typical attack submarines before the use of atomic energy. They could travel underwater for only a few miles at less than five knots because the submarine had to surface to recharge its batteries from the main *diesel engines.*

Late in World War II, the Germans perfected the *snorkel* to provide air for the diesel engines while the submarine was submerged at periscope depth. This device was later adopted by the United States Navy. Another development was a streamlined submarine that used *hydrogen peroxide* fuel to drive a turbine. These submarines achieved twenty-five knots underwater and ran silently up to five knots.

In 1954 the United States Navy placed its first nuclear-powered submarine, the *Nautilus,* into service. Five years later the navy launched the *George Washington,* the first nuclear submarine capable of launching a Polaris ballistic missile. The United States Navy had 41 such nuclear submarines by 1967.

Many of the American nuclear submarines, such as the *Skipjack,* have smooth hulls without the deck, bridge, railings, deck guns, or any other of the protuberances typical of older submarines. The *atomic reactor* which supplies steam to the *electric turbo generator* does not need air and does not produce poisonous exhaust gases. The atomic submarine is capable of running for months without surfacing. Where it travels is limited only by international treaty.

In 1957 the first nuclear-powered *Nautilus* made a voyage completely underwater from Panama to San Diego, California, a distance of more than 3,000 miles. The next year the atomic *Seawolf* remained submerged for sixty days. In 1959, a similar submarine, the *Skate,* spent twelve days cruising under the north polar icecap for a distance of about 3,100 miles. These show some of the capabilities of nuclear submarines.   D. A. B./H. P. O.
SEE ALSO: SHIPS, WEAPONS

Subsonic   see Supersonic

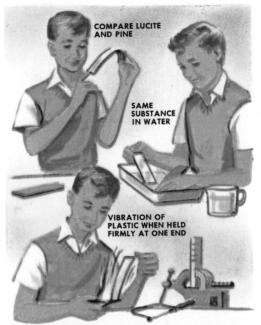

COMPARE LUCITE AND PINE

SAME SUBSTANCE IN WATER

VIBRATION OF PLASTIC WHEN HELD FIRMLY AT ONE END

Substances have many properties which can be determined by simple tests

Substances, properties of The questions asked about a new substance are: What is it like? What will it do if it is bent, heated, or perhaps placed near a magnet? All chemical and physical characteristics of a material are the properties of that material.

The simpler properties are observed in the simplest materials, the chemical elements. For example, if a few properties of oxygen are listed in the order showing the more common first, then the lesser known facts, these facts can be recorded: oxygen is (1) a colorless gas at room temperature; (2) it combines by burning with certain other substances; (3) it becomes a water-clear liquid at $-297.2°$ F; and (4) it is surprisingly magnetic when frozen to its solid state at $-361°$ F.

Other facts that scientists observe about elements are their atomic weight and atomic number and their density, which is the amount of material in them compared with that of a standard substance.

Chemical COMPOUNDS are natural and man-made mixtures which possess much more complicated properties. The research scientist studies new substances to learn what properties they have. Engineers and scientists must know the properties of the mate-

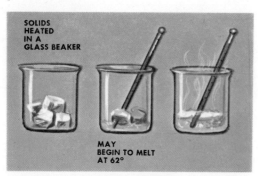

SOLIDS
HEATED
IN A
GLASS BEAKER

MAY
BEGIN TO MELT
AT 62°

rials they work with. Handbooks of chemistry and physics and engineering handbooks carry extensive tables on the properties of various substances.

One good way for the young science student to appreciate properties is for him to select two materials—perhaps a strip of *lucite* plastic and a like-sized piece of pine wood. Next, he should observe as many properties of these two materials as he can. Using the scientific method, he should ask questions beginning with: "What happens when —?" For example; *What happens when* you try to bend each substance? *What happens when* you put each substance in a vessel of water? Many other such "what-happens-when" questions should be devised, then tried out, and recorded.

Properties of materials may be classified under these main heads: (1) *mechanical properties* including bending, stretching, and weight-loading; (2) *chemical properties* such as how substances react chemically; (3) *nuclear or subatomic properties* such as radioactive energy and *half-life.*

These studies of properties show man's wondrous curiosity about his world. The great 19th century scientist, Michael Faraday, wrote a whole book about the properties of common candles.   D. A. B.

SEE ALSO: ELEMENTS, PHYSICAL STATES AND CHANGES

Subtraction see Arithmetic

Subtropic climate see Climate

Succulent plants see Plants, succulent

Sucker see Echinodermata

Sucrose see Carbohydrates, Digestive system, Enzymes

Suffocation see First aid

Sugar Sugars are either sweet or tasteless. As solids they form crystals and are easily dissolved in water. When heated above their melting points, they burn or *char.* Chemists name sugars by several methods. Sugars which cannot be broken apart (*hydrolyzed*) into simpler substances (compounds) are called *simple sugars* or *monosaccharides.* Chains of the same or different simple sugars are called *polysaccharides.* These can be broken into the simple sugars present in them.

Monosaccharides are further classified according to the number of carbon atoms in the sugar molecule. For example, *trioses* have three carbon atoms, *pentoses* five, and *hexoses* six.

Polysaccharides may be classified according to the number of simple sugars, or *residues,* composing them. A *disaccharide* contains two simple sugars bonded together. These two sugars may be alike or different. Examples of disaccharides are *maltose* and *sucrose. Trisaccharides* have three simple sugars linked together. Again, these sugars may be alike or different. Trisaccharides are not as familiar to non-chemists as other sugars. An example, *raffinose,* is stored in many kinds of plants.

Sugars with more than three residues are merely called polysaccharides. Starch found in plants is an example. Plant starch grains (*grana*) are composed of layers of two types of starch surrounded by a thin layer of PROTEIN. The starch responsible for the blue color obtained in the iodine test is *amylose.* Amylose has 200 to 1,000 glucose residues. Glucose is a simple sugar. *Amylopectin,* also part of a starch grain, has several thousand glucose residues. Many of these are long side chains branching off from a main glucose chain at about every twenty-fifth residue. Animal starch (*glycogen*) is similar to amylopectin except that there are more and shorter side chains.

Many of the sugars in food are disaccharides or polysaccharides. ENZYMES in the digestive tract split these complex compounds apart, forming monosaccharides. Water is added to them in order to break them apart. This type of chemical reaction is called *hydrolysis.* Common table sugar is sucrose,

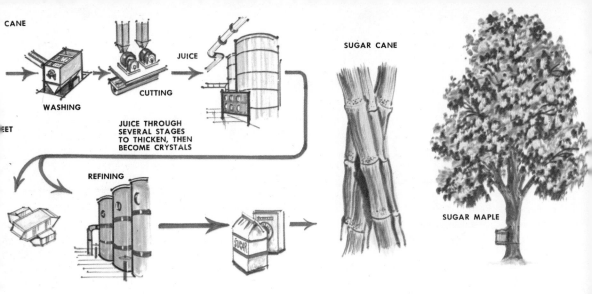

CANE

JUICE

CUTTING

WASHING

EET

JUICE THROUGH
SEVERAL STAGES
TO THICKEN, THEN
BECOME CRYSTALS

REFINING

SUGAR CANE

SUGAR MAPLE

EXTRACTING SUGAR

$$H - \underset{\underset{OH}{|}}{\overset{\overset{H}{|}}{C}} - \underset{\underset{O}{|}}{\overset{\overset{OH}{|}}{C}} - \underset{\underset{H}{|}}{\overset{\overset{H}{|}}{C}} - \underset{\underset{OH}{|}}{\overset{\overset{H}{|}}{C}} - \underset{\underset{OH}{|}}{\overset{\overset{H}{|}}{C}} - H$$

Fructose $C_6H_{12}O_6$

$$\underset{\underset{O}{|}}{\overset{\overset{H}{|}}{C}} - \underset{\underset{H}{|}}{\overset{\overset{OH}{|}}{C}} - \underset{\underset{OH}{|}}{\overset{\overset{H}{|}}{C}} - \underset{\underset{OH}{|}}{\overset{\overset{H}{|}}{C}} - \underset{\underset{OH}{|}}{\overset{\overset{H}{|}}{C}} - \underset{\underset{OH}{|}}{\overset{\overset{H}{|}}{C}} - H$$

Glucose $C_6H_{12}O_6$

SUGARS MAY DIFFER BY CHANGES IN THE
POSITIONS OF [H +] [O =] and [OH −]
ATOMS. SHIFTS IN THE ATOMS ON
CARBONS 1 AND 2 MAKE THE DIFFERENCES
BETWEEN FRUCTOSE AND GLUCOSE

SUGAR BEETS IN THE FIELD

composed of one molecule of glucose and one of fructose (fruit sugar).

Much maltose comes from the breakdown of starch. It is composed of two molecules of glucose. Milk sugar or *lactose* hydrolyzes into one molecule of glucose and one of *galactose*.

All of the monosaccharides enter the intestinal CAPILLARIES and eventually are taken to the LIVER. Enzymes in the liver catalyze or control reactions which change most of the monosaccharides into glucose. Glucose is used by cells in the body to furnish energy for bodily activities.

All of the six-carbon or hexose monosaccharides, such as glucose, have the formula $C_6H_{12}O_6$. Chemists have several methods of graphically representing these different sugars. Such representations are called *structural formulas*. Side groups coming off the main carbon chain are either single *hydrogens* or OH⁻ groups. These come off in different directions in the same way as branches come off a main tree trunk. Thus the sugars differ in chemico-physical properties

according to the plane of their H⁺ or OH⁻ attachments to the main carbon chain.

Aside from a straight chain, these sugars may form *cyclic* or ring molecules. The chain is bent into a ring with an oxygen attached to the first carbon and to either carbons four or five in the chain. Sugars may also rotate the plane of polarized light to the left (−)or to the right (+). Glucose molecules in solution have about five different molecular configurations.

Most table sugar comes either from stems of sugarcane, a MONOCOTYLEDON in the grass family, or from the roots of sugar beets, a DICOTYLEDON in the goosefoot family. Sticks of cane or beets are washed, shredded, and pressed. The sap is purified and crystalized. Sucrose also comes from sorghum and sugar maples.   J. C. K.

SEE ALSO: CARBOHYDRATES, CELLULOSE, DIGESTIVE SYSTEM, PLANT, STARCH

HOW A SULFA DRUG STOPS BACTERIAL GROWTH

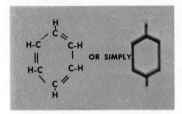

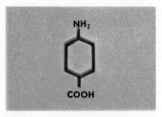

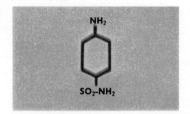

Benzene (6-carbon) ring; the core of sulfa and many other organic chemicals

Para-amino-benzoic acid, a B-vitamin which bacteria seek for their normal growth

The similar sulfa molecule is mistakenly taken up by the bacteria, but they slowly become poisoned by it

Sulfa drugs The sulfa drugs are a group of coal-tar chemicals used to cure certain bacterial diseases. These drugs kill *streptococcus* germs which attack the blood, the skin, the throat, and many parts of the body. Bacterial (not *virus*) *pneumonia* is cured by one kind of sulfa drug.

Sulfanilamide, the first of these drugs to be discovered, was developed from a synthetic red dye called *prontosil.* Dyes had been used before to treat diseases; but they had been able to kill only certain animal types of *microorganisms,* such as the PRO-TOZOA causing amebic dysentery and SLEEP-ING SICKNESS.

Streptococcus microbes and other true bacteria are plantlike *microorganisms.* The problem of researchers was to find chemicals that would kill such BACTERIA. It was observed that *molecules* of sulfanilamide are constructed almost exactly like those of a vitamin-like substance (*para-amino-benzoic acid*) that bacteria need to live. When the bacteria take in sulfanilamide instead, they die.

After sulfanilamide proved successful, other still more effective *sulfonamides* were discovered. Chemists and biologists learned to attach various elements to the basic -SO₂-N- part of sulfonamide molecules, so that the resulting new chemicals would kill certain bacteria. *Sulfadiazine* was thus formed and used against streptococcus germs in *lymph glands,* whereas *sulfathiazole* has been most effective against intestinal bacteria. Today, more than a dozen sulfa drugs are used by doctors.   D. A. B.

SEE ALSO: ANTIBIOTICS, DRUGS, ORGANIC COMPOUNDS, PHARMACOLOGY

Sulfides The sulfides are a group of chemical compounds which contain sulfur. Probably the most familiar compound in the group is poisonous hydrogen sulfide (H_2S) which is a gas with a powerful odor like that of rotten eggs. Hydrogen sulfide has the property of reacting with metal salts, such as copper, zinc, and lead to form insoluble sulfides. The formation of these sulfides are used in chemical analysis for these metals.

Zinc sulfide (ZnS) is used in paints and X ray screens. Red mercuric sulfide is used for coloring wax, plastics, and other materials. Most of the familiar sulfides are gray to black in color and powdery. M. S.

Sulfur Sulfur is the 16th element. It usually is described as a fine, yellow, tasteless, and odorless powder. There are, however, several different forms of sulfur known. In the free state, and as SULFIDES and *sulfates,* sulfur is 0.05% of the earth's crust. Sulfur is used mainly in the manufacture of other chemicals and in the pharmaceutical industry. The old name for sulfur is *brimstone.*

The three major types of sulfur are the *rhombic, monoclinic,* and *amorphous.* Rhombic and monoclinic sulfur have a definite crystal structure. The rhombic is amber in color; the monoclinic is light yellow. The amorphous form is a fine powder or a smooth solid. Sulfur is not

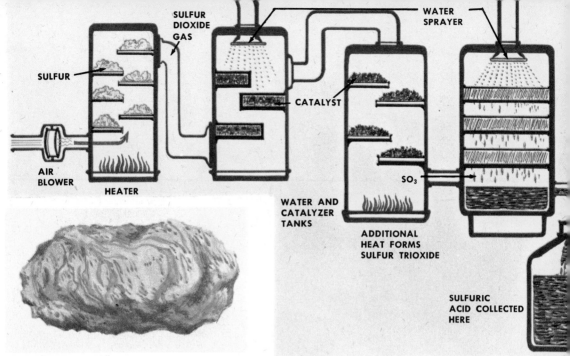

SULFUR DIOXIDE GAS

WATER SPRAYER

SULFUR

CATALYST

AIR BLOWER

HEATER

WATER AND CATALYZER TANKS

SO₃

ADDITIONAL HEAT FORMS SULFUR TRIOXIDE

SULFURIC ACID COLLECTED HERE

Sulfur

Sulfuric acid is made industrially in one way by the contact process

soluble in water and only slightly soluble in alcohol. However, it is very soluble in a sulfur-containing *solvent* called *carbon disulfide*.

Sulfur reacts readily with such active elements as HYDROGEN, FLUORINE and SODIUM, but needs higher temperature or special conditions to react with less active materials. It is used in the manufacture of SULFURIC ACID, *carbon disulfide, gunpowder* and MATCHES, and in bleaching wool and wood pulp. Sulfur, itself, is used in ointments and lotions to remove hardened or dead skin and to fight FUNGUS and RINGWORM.

Sulfur (symbol S) has an atomic weight of 32.066 (32.064, O = 16).   M. S.

SEE ALSO: ATOM, ELEMENTS

Sulfuric acid (suhl-FYOUR-ik) It is a colorless, odorless, heavy liquid. Full-strength acid has great attraction for water and will thus dry air and other gases. This acid has many other uses such as making EXPLOSIVES, other acids, FERTILIZERS, important sulfate salts. Many kinds of sulfur-containing ORGANIC COMPOUNDS can also be made from it.

This powerful acid can cause severe burns to the skin and must be handled with care. In diluting sulfuric acid with water, the acid must always be added to

the water because the opposite addition will create violent sputtering and steaming. The formula is H_2SO_4; the molecular weight is 98.08.   M. S.

SEE ALSO: ACIDS AND BASES

Sumac (SHOO-mack) Sumac is a tree or shrub in genus *Rhus* of the *cashew* family. The leaves are usually compound and turn bright red in fall. The flowers and fruit form in clusters.

The *staghorn, smooth* and *shining sumacs* have large green *panicles* (long flower clusters). The fruit that develops from these is red. The reproductive organs of poison sumac are similar except the poisonous fruit is gray-white. POISON IVY also belongs to the sumac group.

The leaves of sumac are dried and *tannin* is extracted. The galls from certain oriental sumacs are used in making inks.   H. J. C.

Summer see Seasons

Sumac

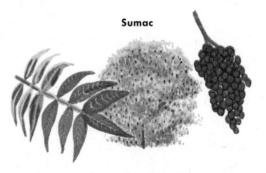

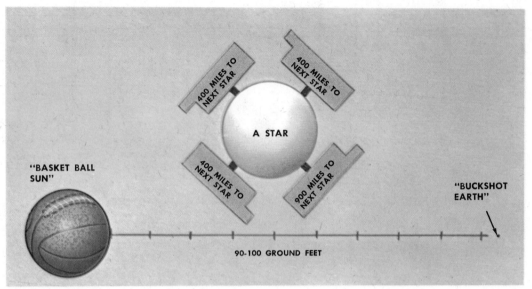

Distances between stars are still amazingly large when the sun is considered to be the size of a basketball and Earth the size of a BB

Sun The sun is a star like most of the little pinpoints of light that are seen at night. If the sun and the other stars were the size of salt grains, the distance from one to the next would be about five miles. If stars were the size of ping pong balls, the separations between stars would be over four hundred miles.

Bringing the sun's size up to that of a basketball, Earth would appear as a BB or buckshot. The 93,000,000 miles from Earth to the sun would then be about one hundred feet. The other stars that are closest would then be about five thousand miles away.

The sun is a member of a large group of stars called a *galaxy*. There are 10 billion stars in the pancake-shaped MILKY WAY, man's galaxy.

The sun is situated on one of the arms of this spiral galaxy, about half-way between the edge of the galaxy and the center.

Of all the stars which have been studied, more than half have a partner or two and go around one an-

other. Many are pairs or groups and orbit around one another, but they appear in the sky as single points of light. The sun does not have another star for a partner. It has a family of planets, called the *solar system*. The sun contains nearly all the material in the family, 99.8%.

HYDROGEN-CLOUD THEORY OF SUN'S ORIGIN

According to one theory, the planets are probably what was left over when the sun was formed out of a huge gas cloud. If the gas cloud had been larger, or contained more, the solar system might have been different. The gas cloud from which the sun was formed, by this theory was mostly hydrogen gas. HYDROGEN is the simplest element in nature. It is very light, and hardly any of it is found in uncombined form on Earth. The most familiar form of hydrogen is in its combined form with oxygen as water. It is present in many other materials, but can be found only in small amounts as a pure gas.

The sun originated as a vast cloud of hydrogen suspended in space. Great quantities of this hydrogen abound but in one place there was some crowding. Even so, the atoms of the gas were spread far apart in SPACE.

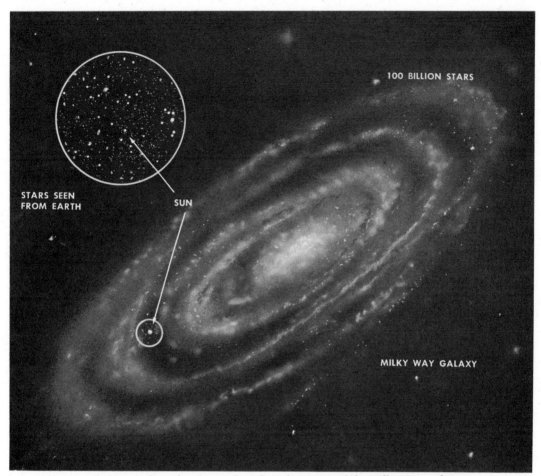

STARS SEEN FROM EARTH

SUN

100 BILLION STARS

MILKY WAY GALAXY

The sun and its planets are thought to be a part of the Milky Way galaxy

The ever-present pull of gravitation began to cause the cloud to collapse. However, the cloud was so vast and the bits of hydrogen were so far apart that the movement was very slow at first. As the distance was lessened between the hydrogen particles, gravitational pull increased. With more force then pulling on the particles to increase their speed and bring them together, the cloud shrank in size but increased in density.

The main pull in the cloud was toward its center where crowded and crashing atoms of hydrogen packed together. Those atoms still coming in were attracted even more by the center clump.

No one from somewhere else would be able to tell that a sun was being formed. No light had yet been given off. The sun was still a *protostar,* a star in formation.

Telescopic photographs of what are considered to be new stars in the sky always appear in very dusty and cloudy-looking places.

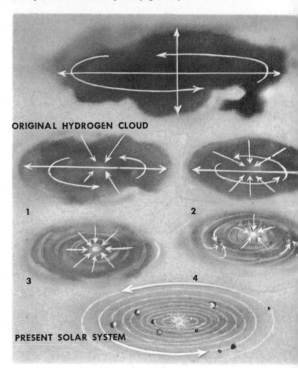

ORIGINAL HYDROGEN CLOUD

1

2

3

4

PRESENT SOLAR SYSTEM

Artist's conception of the hydrogen cloud forming the sun; the gas is beginning to burn

The sun lies somewhere between the red giants and the white dwarfs in age and size

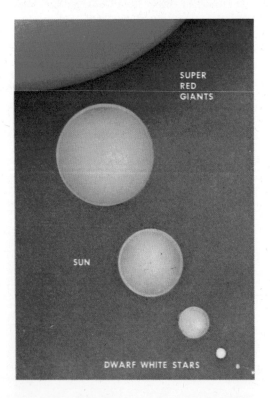

As the hydrogen continued to contract, the gravitational potential energy was converted into heat energy. This increased the temperature of the entire gas mass. When the central mass temperature reached about 500,000° K (Kelvin temperature), the first nuclear reaction could start. This further increased the temperature of the central mass, and the final hydrogen-to-helium reaction (which still is taking place) started.

The major amount of the sun's energy is supplied by this hydrogen-helium, or proton-to-proton, reaction. However, a considerable amount of energy also is liberated by the *carbon cycle*. In this cycle, the process of converting hydrogen to helium starts with ordinary CARBON, C^{12}, which goes through a number of transformations, and finally is converted back to C^{12}, having transformed four hydrogen nuclei into one helium nucleus during the transformations. For stars more massive than the sun, the carbon cycle is thought to be the most important energy cycle.

HOW THE PLANETS FORMED ACCORDING TO THE CLOUD THEORY

Most of the cloud matter formed the sun. The rest went into *protoplanets,* planets

The sun is about in the middle of the range of star characteristics: color, temperature and mass

in formation, which eventually moved to the present orbits and solidified into the PLANETS. Looking down on the solar system from above it, it spins counterclockwise; even the planets spin counterclockwise. The original solar cloud must have had this direction of spin.

The sun rotates this way, too, about once every 27 days. Its equator spins faster than its poles, proving that it is not a solid body.

The period of the sun's rotation can be actually measured by studying SUNSPOTS. Those nearest the poles do not move as quickly as those at the sun's equator.

THE SUN COMPARED TO OTHER STARS

There are enough stars so the astronomers can compare and find that the sun is about average in many ways. In scientific consideration of mass or density of the sun, it is seen that there are stars with ten times as

much mass, and some with only one tenth. However, sizes are another factor. The largest red supergiant stars would nearly fill up the space of the solar system out to the orbit of SATURN. The very dense white dwarfs are only the size of the EARTH. The sun is as massive on the average as water. Its center is ten times more massive than lead.

The big red supergiants are only one-millionth of the density of air, as contrasted with white dwarfs with the same amount of matter so tightly packed that a cubic inch would weigh thousands of tons. Nothing on Earth is packed that densely.

The more massive a star, the brighter it is, and the faster it uses up its hydrogen. The brightest stars are green-white. The sun is a middle-type giving a yellow color. The most feeble lights are from the white dwarfs.

A so-called *main sequence* chart can be made to show the many types of stars and

Solar spectrum

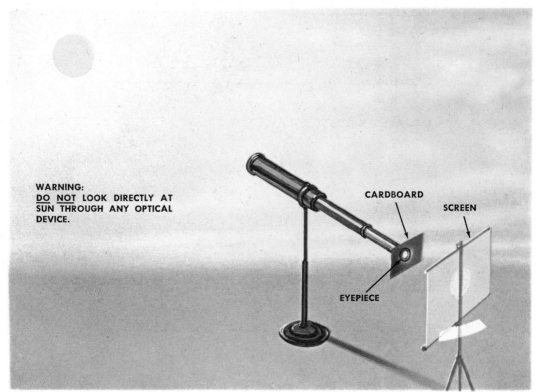

WARNING:
DO <u>NOT</u> LOOK DIRECTLY AT
SUN THROUGH ANY OPTICAL
DEVICE.

CARDBOARD

SCREEN

EYEPIECE

Features of the sun can be observed indirectly through a telescope

how they differ. The sun shows up in the middle of the main sequence. On the main sequence, where the sun is located, brightness increases until a point toward the left where the most luminescent and hot stars are charted. Thus the sun should become more luminous as it ages.

But there are still other types of stars. Other locations on the chart stand for white dwarf stars which are radiating only left-over energy since they have used up their consumable matter. A great quantity of cool, red light comes from a red giant.

The stars in the main sequence are using up their consumable matter at different rates, some fast and some slow depending upon their mass.

The sun's light also tells the kind of atoms (ELEMENTS) of which it is made. The sun's light can be spread apart into a rainbow. In an instrument called a SPEC-TROSCOPE, an enclosed prism or diffraction grating will break the light into its colors and reveal certain parts as darkened lines or bands, called *Fraunhofer Lines*. By their position, the dark bands give evidence of gases. Such lines, either bright or dark, are much like fingerprints of gaseous elements.

The sun's SPECTRUM shows the lines of hydrogen and helium as well as other elements.

A telescope can be used for studying the sun; but only with a special filter is it safe to look at the sun directly. A regular TELESCOPE can be positioned in such a way that the sun's image is projected on a piece of paper or screen. Sunspots can sometimes be seen and traced to check their speed across the surface. If the size of the spots are calculated, it is sometimes a surprise to learn that hundreds of earths would be needed to cover one sunspot. Astronomers have calculated the diameter of the sun to be 864,000 miles.

The sun gives off radiant energy of many wave lengths. White sunlight has a whole range of wave lengths. They are measured in *angstrom* units. One angstrom is equal to 10^{-8} cm. The waves shorter than white light, X-RAYS for example, may be one angstrom. Ultraviolet light is also shorter than the visible kind of light, up to around 3000 angstroms. Most of the sun's ultraviolet light is stopped by the material in the atmosphere before it reaches the surface of the earth.

Radiation with from 3800 to 7500 angstroms is the range of COLORS that make up visible white light. Those longer are infrared or heat waves. Radio waves are even longer. Solar radio waves can be received and turned into audible sound, and man's ears hear only that part of it which is within their range, much as man's eyes see only a tiny portion of the sun's RADIATION which reaches him.

THE NATURE OF SUNSPOTS AND
SUN'S ENERGY

In cycles of about seven years, the sun shows many sunspots for a while. The radio COMMUNICATION on Earth is affected by the sun's behavior. Over parts of the earth near its poles, showers of particles from the sun come into the earth's upper atmosphere and cause the "northern (or southern) lights."

The sun is studied intensely during these active times. Instruments which effectively produce a solar eclipse mask off the bright surface of the sun so that its edges can be photographed. Glowing gas can be seen swirling and shooting from the sun. Only the red portions of light given off by hydrogen are screened through to the film.

The amount of power pouring from the sun is 4×10^{33} ergs per second or 5×10^{23} horsepower. The planets intercept only one part in 100 million of this radiation.

The sun's mass is 333,000 times that of the earth's. The sun's volume is one and one-third million times as large, but it is less dense than the earth.

The PHOTOSPHERE is the visible surface from which a solar spectrum is received. In enlarged photos it is very turbulent. The TEMPERATURE at the surface is about 6000° on the Kelvin scale. The *chromosphere* is a layer up to around 7500 miles above the photosphere. It is reddish from the hydrogen glow. The *corona* is the outer atmosphere of the sun which shows up in total solar eclipses as a feeble light.

In the moving group of stars to which it belongs, the sun is traveling toward Vega (a brilliant white star of the first magnitude), at the rate of about 12 miles per second. In its path around the galaxy, it is going 125 miles per second. F. R. W.

SEE ALSO: AURORA BOREALIS, INTERNATIONAL GEOPHYSICAL YEAR, LIGHT, SOLAR PROTUBERANCES, STAR

Sunburn Skin burned by the sun is really burned by the *ultraviolet rays* in the sun's light. The rays penetrate the outer layers of skin. Large doses can damage the skin cells.

Substances from the injured cells in the epidermis spread to the lower layers. The skin becomes red and sore due to congestion of the blood vessels. Blistering may appear later.

Pigment or coloring matter in the cells is a protection against ultraviolet. People with dark skins burn less easily, since this pigment is distributed throughout the epidermis. People with light skins burn quickly because the pigment is concentrated below the epidermis. Burning is usually followed by tanning. As the skin heals, it thickens and more pigment appears in the cells. Tanning protects against ultraviolet. E. P. L.

Sundew Sundews are also called *dew plants*. Some kinds grow in many places in the world. Most of the 90 species are native to Australia. The plants are *carnivorous*. They can trap and digest insects. Leaves are covered by sticky, sensitive hairs that close the leaf when touched.

If leaf-hairs close by the stimulation of something other than an insect, they open again in a short while. When an insect is trapped, the hairs secrete an enzyme that digests the insect. The leaf remains closed until digestion is complete.

Leaves are often arranged in a rosette growing close to the ground. A long, slender floral stem grows from the center of the rosette. Pink, red or white flowers are clustered on a flower head. Flowers have five petals, five stamens and a five-part ovary that develops into a dry capsule. J. C. K.

Sundew, an insectivorous plant

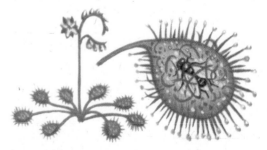

TELLING TIME BY THE SUN

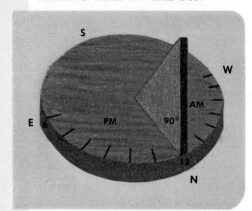

1. Cut the dial face out of a square foot of heavy wood.
2. Cut a wooden triangle with a six-inch base to serve as the gnomon. Nail this on the dial face with the high point on the outside rim.
3. Set the sundial in a permanent place outside in a wide open area. Use a compass to line the gnomon up with the North Pole.
4. When the sun's rays are directly overhead (no shadow on the dial face) letter the number "12" at this point. Continue to mark the numbers as each hour passes.
5. 6:00 A.M. will be west of the low end of the gnomon, while 6:00 P.M. will be east.

Sundial (SUHN-die-uhl) Thousands of years ago, men noticed that as the sun moved across the sky, the shadow it made of a stone or tree moved across the ground. The early *Egyptians* and *Babylonians* learned to put a stick in the ground and mark units of time by it. This was the first sundial.

Later models became more elaborate. The Egyptians of the eighth century B.C. used a horizontal T-shaped object. The cross-bar was raised on a block above the long stem. The cross-bar was placed facing the sun and cast its shadow across the stem, which was marked off into 12 units (hours).

Sundial

Egyptian shadow clock

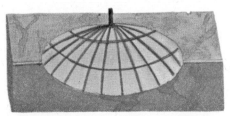

Greek or Roman hemicycle sundial

The Greeks and Romans carved a *hemicycle,* or hollow quarter-sphere, in stone. Lines were drawn on the inside surface and met at a point where the stick, or *gnomon,* was placed. The gnomon is the rod that casts a shadow on the dial. This shadow stick is sometimes called the *style*.

The best-known sundial, used in the 15th century, had a flat, horizontal surface on which were usually marked two concentric circles—one divided into hours, the other into minutes. The gnomon (in the center) was placed at a certain angle with the face. This angle had to equal the *latitude* (angular distance from the equator) on the surface of the earth at which the sundial was located.

Because the sundial was useless in cloudy weather and at night, it was replaced by the modern clock. Today, sundials serve only a decorative purpose, and can often be seen in parks and gardens.   D. A. B.
SEE ALSO: CLOCKS, EARTH, MEASUREMENT, TIME ZONES

Sunfish

Chicago Natural History Museum
Sunfish

Sunflower

Sunfish Several well-known fresh-water fish are called sunfish. Bluegills, breams, crappies and pumpkinseed fish are four common North American kinds. They reach lengths of eight to ten inches, and they live in streams, ponds and lakes.

Sunfish build their nests on river bottoms and lake beds. They lay their egg masses within the nests. The brightly colored male protects the eggs from being eaten by other fish. Sunfish eat smaller fish, shellfish, worms, and insects. Man eats the flesh of the fresh-water sunfish.

The giant ocean sunfish, or *Mola mola,* is tough-fleshed. It is clumsy in its swimming habits. It really suns itself at times, as it floats lazily on the calm ocean surface. Its great, shiny body may grow to ten feet in length and weigh nearly one ton. Other oceanic sunfish, all of family *Molidae,* are smaller than Mola; some of these can puff out their bodies when disturbed.

Fresh-water sunfish are popular for beginners at sport fishing because they take or dodge bait as energetically as do the rarer sporting fish.   D. A. B.
SEE ALSO: BLUEGILL, CRAPPIE

Sunflower The sunflower is an HERB which grows as an annual or a perennial. Some have attained a height of fifteen feet. The LEAVES are oval, hairy, and arranged alternately on the stem. Some sunflowers are weeds, while others are cultivated. It is the state flower of Kansas.

Leaves on this flowering plant may be one foot long. A single FLOWER head may also be a foot wide. It has a *tuber* or underground STEM.

A single flower head is really many individual flowers on one big receptacle. The outer ring (*ray*) flowers are irregularly shaped. Each possesses one long, strap-shaped, yellow "petal." The center (*disk*) flowers may be yellow, brown, purple, or black. Each is regular, having five petals which form a tube. Each has five stamens and one pistil. The latter has two united carpels in which develops a single seed. The FRUIT, an *achene,* is dry and indehiscent.

Oil from sunflower seeds is fed to livestock. *Pepitos* is the name of seeds sold for human consumption. Sunflowers are in the family Compositae.   H. J. C.
SEE ALSO: COMPOSITE FLOWER

Sunset see Tyndall effect

Sunshine recorder Sunshine recorders are several different kinds of instruments used by weather scientists or meteorologists to measure either the amount of time the sun shines during the day or the intensity with which it shines.

Three types of sunshine-duration recorders are now in use. All attempt to record the hours of direct sunlight, but only the *photoelectric* type is sensitive enough to distinguish between a cloudy sky that is very bright and direct sunshine.

The Campbell-Stokes device consists of a glass globe which focuses the light rays of the sun on a card on which a time scale is printed. As the position of the sun changes, a line is burned in the card show-

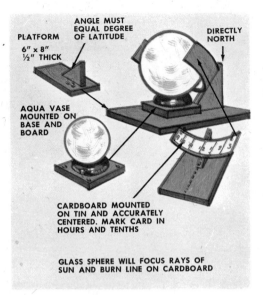

ANGLE MUST
EQUAL DEGREE
OF LATITUDE

PLATFORM

DIRECTLY
NORTH

6" x 8"
½" THICK

AQUA VASE
MOUNTED ON
BASE AND
BOARD

CARDBOARD MOUNTED
ON TIN AND ACCURATELY
CENTERED. MARK CARD IN
HOURS AND TENTHS

GLASS SPHERE WILL FOCUS RAYS OF
SUN AND BURN LINE ON CARDBOARD

A simple sunshine recorder

ing when direct sunshine was visible. This recorder is relatively trouble-free, but becomes inaccurate at sunrise and sunset.

The Maring-Marvin recorder uses a black bulb and clear bulb mounted in a *vacuum tube* to sense the presence of sunshine. As sunlight strikes the black bulb, the heat sends a column of *mercury* up the tube to close an electric switch. The electric contact allows a pen to record the duration of sunshine on a moving drum.

A photoelectric sunshine recorder used by the United States Weather Bureau overcomes the deficiencies of the other types because it contains both a built-in shaded cell and also an unshaded cell. Thus, it constantly measures the difference between shaded light and direct light. When direct sunlight is visible, the direct light effect is greater than that on the shaded cell and the instrument will activate the recording mechanism. When direct sunlight is not visible, however, the difference in intensity between the shaded and unshaded cells is small; therefore, the recording instrument will not be activated.

Sunshine intensity recorders, called *pyroheliometers,* record *solar radiation* by measuring the temperature rise on a silver disk during a specific time. Other instruments use more complicated electric devices that are capable of measuring differences in heat energies absorbed by black bodies.   E. I. D.
SEE ALSO: PHOTOELECTRICITY, WEATHER STATION

Sunspot see Solar protuberances

Sunstroke see First aid

Supersaturated solutions (soo-puhr-SATCH-uh-rate-ed) A solution, such as sugar in water, can only keep dissolved a certain amount of this sugar at a given temperature. It is generally true that with increasing temperature more *solute* (sugar) can stay dissolved. However, if a saturated solution at a temperature of 100° F is cooled to 90° F, the solute may tend to stay in solution though it is beyond the saturation point. This is called a super saturated solution.

A supersaturated solution is very unstable. Upon the addition of a crystal of the solute, the extra amount of solute will crystallize out of the solution, leaving a saturated solution in its place.   M. S.
SEE ALSO: SOLUBILITY, SOLVENT

Supersonic (soo-per-SAHN-ik) Supersonic refers to speeds faster than the speed of sound. The speed of sound is called *Mach 1* by the aircraft designers. Mach 1 is about 760 miles per hour at sea level.

In *subsonic* flight, an aircraft wing forms a pressure area in front of it, which assists the air to flow smoothly around the wing. As the aircraft approaches the *transonic* speed range, or approximately the speed of sound, the behavior of the air changes drastically. It does not move out of the way of the wing fast enough. This results in the air being compressed violently, creating a "shock" or "compression wave." These unstable shock waves create tremendous drag and buffeting of the aircraft.

Once supersonic speeds are reached, the shock waves become stabilized and the aircraft may achieve smooth, easily-controlled flight. Aircraft designers have developed the swept-back wing and highly streamlined shapes to assist in going through the transonic speed range into supersonic flight. Strange-appearing design features, such as the area rule principle which narrows the *fuselage* at the point where it is joined by the wings, has established relia-

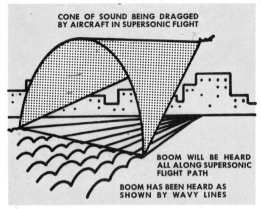

A sonic boom is caused by shock waves that build up around an aircraft flying at supersonic speeds

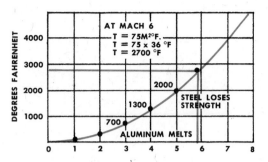

Problems of extremely high temperatures produced by friction arise during flight at supersonic speeds. At high altitudes, where air is thin, speeds of Mach 7 or 8 (7 or 8 times the speed of sound) are possible

bility and safety in supersonic flight.

Engineers and scientists are now working on a new "barrier" which must be solved as aircraft are being designed for greater supersonic speeds. This is the thermal barrier, and concerns the tremendously high temperatures created by an aircraft, or object, flying through the air at extremely high speed.

The shock wave created by an aircraft in supersonic flight may occasionally extend to the ground and be heard as a sharp explosive sound as it passes along the path of flight. This shock wave is called a *sonic boom.*

Designers of *steam turbines,* high-speed gunnery *projectiles,* and other high-speed flight objects are also faced with problems of supersonic *aerodynamics.*   R. J. J.

SEE ALSO: AERODYNAMICS; AIR; FLIGHT, PRINCIPLES OF; SOUND; SOUND BARRIER

Surface tension (SUHR-fuss TEN-shun) To understand surface tension, one must think of the large number of MOLECULES in, for instance, a glass of water. A molecule of water in the middle of this glass is acted upon fairly evenly by all the molecules around it. A molecule of water at the surface, however, is only partly surrounded and is attracted downward toward the main body of water. This downward attraction causes a strain at the surface of the liquid, called surface tension.

The surface tension behavior of liquids is what causes drops of water to form as *spheres* and allows metal foils to float on liquid surfaces. Surface tension can be determined by the amount a given liquid rises in a very thin tube called a *capillary,* by measuring the force needed to pull a standard wire ring, usually *platinum,* from a surface, or by measuring the pressure necessary to form a bubble in a liquid.

Materials called *surface active agents,* which are actually the everyday soaps and laundry *detergents,* lower the surface tension of water. This lowering of the surface tension allows the water to penetrate fabrics and skin.

Surface tension is usually measured in *dynes* per centimeter. Water has the value of 72 at room temperature. The strength of the surface tension varies with the COHESION of the liquid.   M. S.

SEE ALSO: CAPILLARITY, DETERGENT, MOLECULAR THEORY, WETTING AGENT

Surface tension differs in various liquids

DYNES REQUIRED TO PULL A ONE CENTIMETER RING FROM THE SURFACE

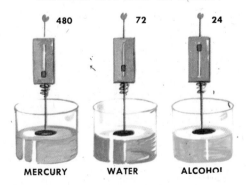

Trephining, an ancient surgical operation, was used to release "evil spirits" from the body

Surgery Surgery attempts to correct physical disabilities, repair injuries, and to treat such diseases as may respond to physical measures. The practice of present day surgery requires a knowledge of all the basic sciences of medicine and an understanding of new phases of clinical medicine.

Surgery had its beginning in the treatment of accidents and injuries. It soon advanced to be the treatment of certain serious diseases. This advance developed rapidly when man learned to work metals and fashion useful tools. Ancient Egyptian mummies have been found with holes cut through the skull, a procedure thought to be used to let out evil spirits when man's mind was affected. This operation is called a *trephination.*

Progress in surgery was continuous, although when compared with today's knowledge, its early development into a scientific practice seems slow. The periods of brilliant successes were counteracted by whole centuries wherein little headway was gained. One reason seemed to be the lack of communication between the workers in surgery of one country with those of another.

When the universities of the Middle Ages in Italy, France, and England established schools of medicine, surgery began to make new progress. One of the difficulties to be overcome included legal restrictions on a study of human ANATOMY through dissection. There needed to be a resolution of the different methods used in surgical technique; as, for example, the proper place of the cautery versus cutting. Unknown for a long time also was the kind of treatment for complications such as bleeding and the formation of pus in the operative area. Overshadowing all of this, perhaps, was the need for an anesthetic, some safe agent to permit painless surgery.

To gain experience and knowledge in anatomy certain countries turned over to surgeons the bodies of executed criminals. The problem of hemorrhage, which had long been treated by cautery, was solved when AMBROISE PARÉ, a French barber-surgeon born about 1510, started the use of *ligatures,* tying off blood vessels by strands of hair and thread.

Pus at the operative site remained a problem for a long time. Its presence seemed inevitable, and it was even called "laudable" pus. It was thought to be a sure sign of good healing. This idea continued until JOSEPH LISTER became Chief-of-Surgery at the University of Glasgow. There, appalled by the great prevalence of "hospital gangrene," he began to insist that the presence of pus was not necessary in surgical cases. Encouraged by PASTEUR'S earlier work on fermentation, he demanded the strictest cleanliness in the operating rooms and wards. He reasoned that by destroying the bacteria present in pus infections, healing would take place when the tissues were first brought together. He advanced the idea of antisepsis, accomplished by spraying sheets hung in the operating rooms with carbolic acid. As the idea spread through the medical world, it was soon superseded by *asepsis,* which simply means *clean, clean, clean* with no contamination.

The need for a helpful agent to abolish pain in surgical procedures had been obvious from the very beginning. The more extensive surgical work became, the more the necessity was realized. Experiments with sleeping potions had gone on from earliest times. Extracts were made from the seed of the poppy (opium) and combined with mandragora (May apple) and Indian hemp and used to induce sleep.

Probably one of the greatest contributions America has made to medicine was the use of ETHER for surgical operations. Ether was first used by Crawford W. Long on March 30, 1842, at Athens, Jackson County, Georgia. In England the first to use ether was the father-in-law of Joseph Lister, Robert Liston, in 1846. Robert Liston was a Scotsman who was Professor of Clinical Surgery at University College, London.

Thus by the middle of the 19th century,

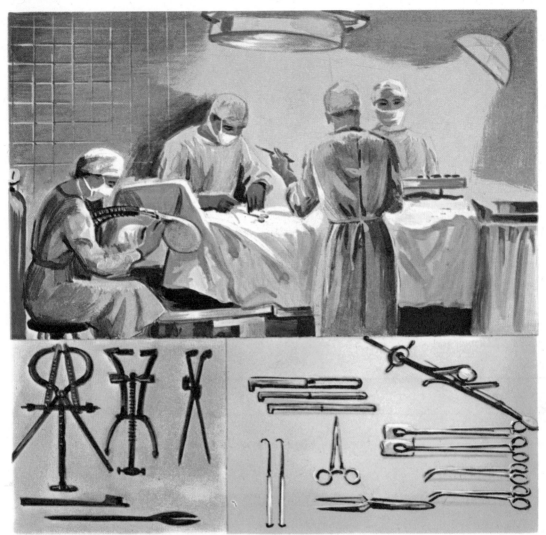

A modern operating room (top) and modern surgical tools (bottom right); surgeon's table found in the ruins of Pompeii (bottom left)

surgery was prepared to make the phenomenal advances known today. Having overcome the pain of operation with anesthesia, and infection with ANTISEPTICS and the broad spectrum of ANTIBIOTICS now in use, the last 100 years unquestionably represent the greatest period in surgical history. The most hidden parts of the body can be explored without the danger of infection, and extreme haste is no longer necessary.

Surgery today is subdivided into numerous specialties, such as orthopedic surgery, heart surgery, lung surgery, and plastic surgery. The American Board of Surgery and the various surgical societies certify to their members' capabilities after searching investigation and examination.

New instruments and new devices contin-ually open up new horizons. The heart-lung machine, the artifical kidney, hypothermic devices to enable body temperature to be reduced so that certain operations, as on the heart, can be performed, ultrasonic waves and electronic machines all have proven helpful in one field or another.

The general trend of medicine and surgery today calls for close unity of thought and purpose of all the medical disciplines. It is a team approach in which the clinician, the surgeon, the pathologist, the radiologist, and other specialists all collaborate. They must know enough of the other fields to be aware of the contributions of each, to the end that the best interests of the sick shall be served. H. K. S.

SEE ALSO: MEDICINE, PATHOLOGY